the source
2

the worship collection compiled by
Graham Kendrick

Kevin
Mayhew

First published in Great Britain in 2001 by world wide worship
Buxhall, Stowmarket, Suffolk IP14 3BW
Tel 01449 737978 E-mail www@kevinmayhewltd.com

Compilation © world wide worship 2001

Acknowledgements

The publishers wish to express their gratitude to the copyright holders who have granted permission to include their material in this book.

Every effort has been made to trace the copyright holders of all the songs in this collection and we hope that no copyright has been infringed. Apology is made and pardon sought if the contrary be the case, and a correction will be made in any reprint of this book.

Important Copyright Information

We would like to remind users of this hymnal that the reproduction of any song texts or music without the permission of the copyright holder is illegal. Details of all copyright holders are clearly indicated under each song.

Most of the song texts are covered by a Christian Copyright Licensing (CCL) licence. If you possess a CCL licence, it is essential that you check your instruction manual to ensure that the song you wish to use is covered.

If you are not a member of CCL, or the song you wish to reproduce is not covered by your licence, you must contact the copyright holder direct for their permission.

Christian Copyright Licensing (Europe) Ltd have also now introduced a Music Reproduction Licence. Again, if you hold such a licence it is essential that you check your instruction manual to ensure that the song you wish to reproduce is covered. The reproduction of any music not covered by your licence is both illegal and immoral.

If you are interested in joining CCL they can be contacted at the following address:

Christian Copyright Licensing (Europe) Ltd, P.O. Box 1339, Eastbourne,
East Sussex BN 21 1AD. Tel: 01323 417711, Fax: 01323 417722.

Scripture quotations taken from the HOLY BIBLE, NEW INTERNATIONAL VERSION.
Copyright © 1973, 1978, 1984 by International Bible Society.
Used by permission of Hodder & Stoughton Limited. All rights reserved.

The right of Graham Kendrick to be identified as the compiler of this work has been asserted by him in accordance with the Copyright, Designs and Patents Act 1988.

The following editions are available:

Combined Words edition	Catalogue No. 1470102
	ISBN No. 1 84003 726 1
	ISMN No. M 57004 861 8
Music Edition	Catalogue No. 1470105
	ISBN No. 1 84003 724 5
	ISMN No. M 57004 859 5
Guitarists' Edition	Catalogue No. 1470112
	ISBN No. 1 84003 725 3
	ISMN No. M 57004 860 1

Foreword

This is no follow-up volume! **the source 2** complements the original volume of **the source** with material drawn from all over the English-speaking world, providing worship groups, musicians and leaders with a compilation that is refreshingly international.

We found a blessing in the process of compiling **the source 2** songbook by being exposed to the breadth of worship material flowing in from churches of very diverse worship style and emphasis worldwide. It has been said that it will require the cumulative effect of the best worship of every Christian community, great and small, in every language and culture everywhere, to even begin to expound adequately the multifaceted glories of Christ. Indeed, the book of Revelation stirs anticipation of such a thing. Each Christian community has the potential of some distinct and special worship offering.

At the same time, each needs its vision of Christ expanded by what the other communities bring.

Not only did we seek breadth, we looked for depth; for rich and trustworthy content, and for height; songs which lift us out of ourselves and fill our vision with the attributes of God. Alongside the new, we added to the treasury of traditional hymns those not usually found between the same pair of covers, some of which sport new melodies.

Having said all this, a farmer can only harvest what has grown, and there are still too few new writers exploring the 'deeper' and the 'higher', and many vital themes of the faith seem almost entirely overlooked. The disproportionate number of 'subjective experience' songs being written begs the question of how much the world's agenda of placing existential experience and individual fulfilment at the centre of things has influenced our worship. The man who said 'You sing me your songs and I'll tell you your theology' was definitely onto something!

Worship songs remain one of the few ways through which biblical truth is memorised today, and the enormous popularity of praise and worship songs is an opportunity for edifying the Church by inculcating good teaching through them, provided we are thoughtful and discerning in our choices. We may exercise a degree of influence as compilers, but the real power is where the rubber hits the road, each time a pastor or worship leader compiles a song list. Use it well!

GRAHAM KENDRICK
Compiler

JONATHAN BUGDEN
RICHARD LEWIS
MATTHEW LOCKWOOD
Compiling Team

611 Above all

Words and Music: Lenny LeBlanc and Paul Baloche

A-bove all pow - ers, a-bove all kings, a-bove all

na - ture and all cre-a - ted things; a-bove all

wis - dom and all the ways of man,

you were here be-fore the world be-gan. A - bove all

king - doms,   a -bove all   thrones,   a - bove all

won - ders the world   has e - ver known;   a - bove all

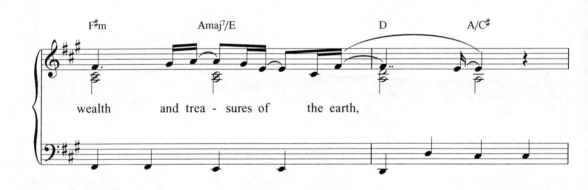

wealth   and trea - sures of   the earth,

there's no way   to mea - sure what   you're worth.

Cru - ci-fied, laid be-hind the stone; you

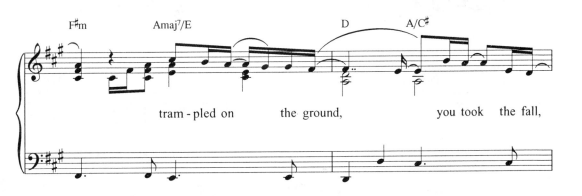

lived to die, re - ject-ed and a-lone; like a rose,

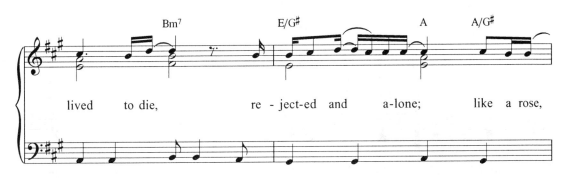

tram - pled on the ground, you took the fall,

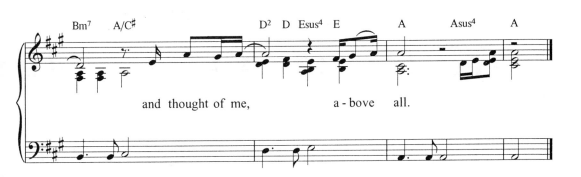

and thought of me, a - bove all.

612 Alas! and did my Saviour bleed   *(At the cross)*

Words: Isaac Watts and Ralph E. Hudson,
based on Matthew 27: 35-50

Music: Ralph E. Hudson

1. Alas! and did my Saviour bleed and did my Sov-'reign die? Would he de-vote that sa-cred head for sin-ners such as I? At the cross, at the cross where I first saw the light and the bur-den of my heart rolled a-way. It was

there by faith I re-ceived my sight, and now I am hap-py all the day!

2. Was it for crimes that I have done
   he groaned upon the tree?
   Amazing pity! Grace unknown!
   And love beyond degree!

3. But drops of grief can ne'er repay
   the debt of love I owe:
   here, Lord, I give myself away,
   'tis all that I can do!

To him who is able to keep you from falling
and to present you before his glorious presence
without fault and with great joy –
to the only God our Saviour
be glory, majesty, power and authority,
through Jesus Christ our Lord, before all ages,
now and for evermore! Amen.

Jude 24-25

613 All around the world

Words and Music: Paul Oakley

614 All creatures of our God and King

Words: William Henry Draper, alt.
based on the *Cantico di Frate Sole* of
St. Francis of Assisi

Music: *Geistliche Kirchengesang*, Cologne
arr. Ralph Vaughan Williams

LASST UNS ERFREUEN 88 44 88 and Alleluias

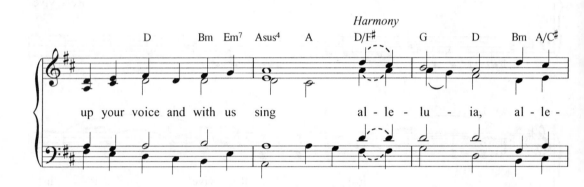

1. All crea-tures of our God and King, lift

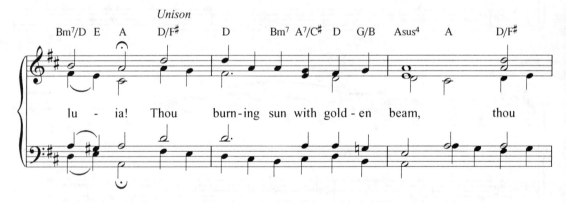

up your voice and with us sing al-le-lu-ia, al-le-

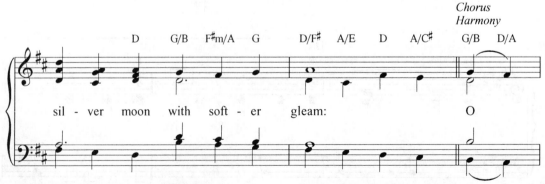

lu-ia! Thou burn-ing sun with gold-en beam, thou

sil-ver moon with soft-er gleam: O

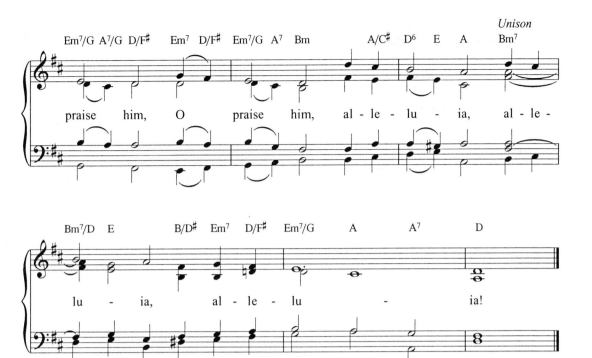

praise him, O praise him, al - le - lu - ia, al - le -

lu - ia, al - le - lu - ia!

2. Thou rushing wind that art so strong,
   ye clouds that sail in heav'n along,
   O praise him, alleluia!
   Thou rising morn, in praise rejoice,
   ye lights of evening, find a voice:

3. Thou flowing water, pure and clear,
   make music for thy Lord to hear,
   alleluia, alleluia!
   Thou fire so masterful and bright,
   that givest us both warmth and light:

4. And all ye men of tender heart,
   forgiving others, take your part,
   O sing ye, alleluia!
   Ye who long pain and sorrow bear,
   praise God and on him cast your care:

5. Let all things their Creator bless,
   and worship him in humbleness,
   O praise him, alleluia!
   Praise, praise the Father, praise the Son,
   and praise the Spirit, Three in One.

615 Alleluia, alleluia

(Agnus Dei)

Words and Music: Michael W. Smith

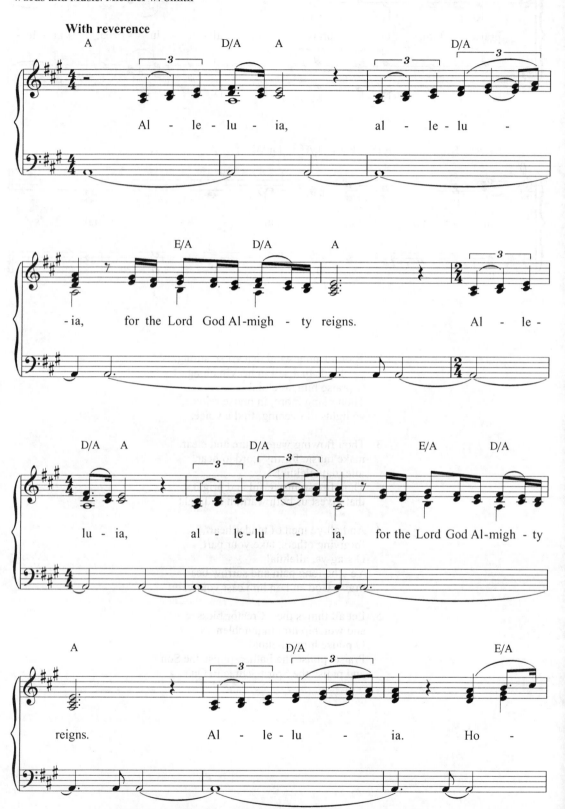

Al - le - lu - ia, al - le - lu - ia, for the Lord God Al-migh - ty reigns. Al - le - lu - ia, al - le - lu - ia, for the Lord God Al-migh - ty reigns. Al - le - lu - ia. Ho -

ly,   ho - ly   are you, Lord God   Al - migh-

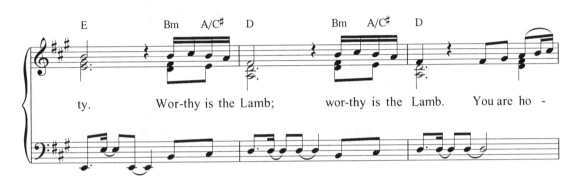

ty.   Wor-thy is the Lamb;   wor-thy is the Lamb.   You are ho -

ly.   Ho - ly   are you, Lord God   Al - migh - ty.   Wor-thy is the

Lamb;   wor-thy is the Lamb.   You are ho - Lamb;   A - men.

616 Alleluia, sing to Jesus

Words: William Chatterton Dix, alt.

Music: Rowland Hugh Prichard
arr. Ralph Vaughan Williams

HYFRYDOL 87 87 D

1. Al - le - lu - ia, sing to Je - sus, his the scep - tre, his the throne; al - le - lu - ia, his the tri - umph, his the vic - to - ry a - lone: hark, the songs of peace - ful Si - on thun - der like a

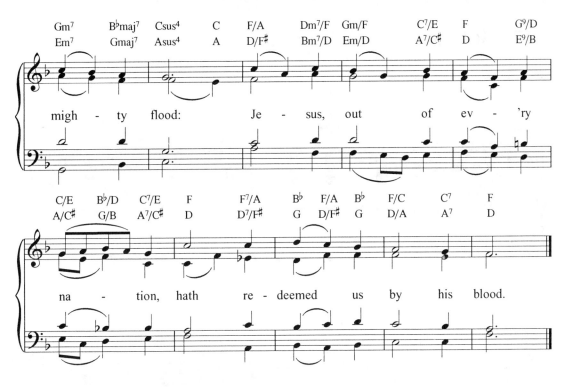

migh - ty flood: Je - sus, out of ev - 'ry
na - tion, hath re - deemed us by his blood.

2. Alleluia, not as orphans
   are we left in sorrow now;
   alleluia, he is near us,
   faith believes, nor questions how;
   though the cloud from sight received him
   when the forty days were o'er,
   shall our hearts forget his promise,
   'I am with you evermore'?

3. Alleluia, bread of angels,
   here on earth our food, our stay;
   alleluia, here the sinful
   come to you from day to day.
   Intercessor, friend of sinners,
   earth's redeemer, plead for me,
   where the songs of all the sinless
   sweep across the crystal sea.

4. Alleluia, King eternal,
   he the Lord of lords we own;
   alleluia, born of Mary,
   earth his footstool, heav'n his throne;
   he within the veil has entered
   robed in flesh, our great High Priest;
   he on earth both priest and victim
   in the Eucharistic Feast.

617 All I have

Words and Music: Mark Altrogge

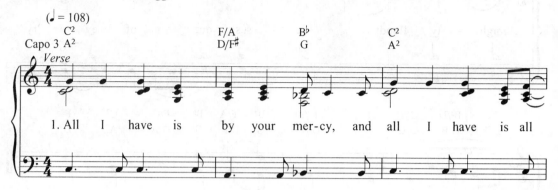

1. All I have is by your mer-cy, and all I have is all

of grace. All I am is what your love has

made of me. Now I am your

new cre-a-tion, your work-man-ship in Je-sus Christ.

2. All I have is from you, Father,
   the Author of each perfect gift.
   You gladly give me all things
   to enjoy in you.
   You who did not spare your Son
   but freely gave him for us all,
   will you not with joy supply
   my ev'ry need?

618 All I have in this world

(Kiss your feet)

Words and Music: Martin Smith
arr. Dave Bankhead

is - n't   he   beau - ti - ful?

To next verse

Last time

3. Take   this

2. All I have in this life
   is all for a King you know I live for.
   And your crown bears my name
   for I was born to give you praise.
   Isn't he beautiful . . .

3. Take this life; take it all
   I'm breathing the dirt, but I have clean hands
   so I'll run with my boots on
   for I was born to give you fame.
   Yes, you are beautiful . . .

619 All I want is to know you, Jesus
(Nothing is as wonderful)

Words and Music: Scott Underwood

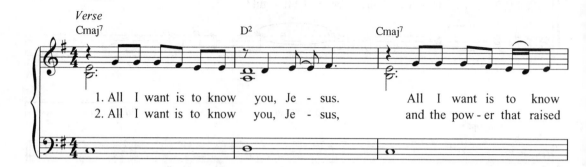

1. All I want is to know you, Je - sus. All I want is to know
2. All I want is to know you, Je - sus, and the pow - er that raised

I be-long to you. Show me all of the things that are worth - less,
you from the dead. Help me for - get all the things that I've done.

that I thought were so val - ua - ble to you. No-thing is as love-ly,
Set my heart on what lies a - head.

no-thing is as wor-thy, no-thing is as won-der-ful as know-ing you.

No-thing is as love-ly, no-thing is as wor-thy, no-thing is as won-der - ful

1. as know-ing you.

2. as know-ing you, as know - ing you,

as know-ing you.

Therefore God exalted him to the highest place
and gave him the name that is above every name,
that at the name of Jesus every knee should bow,
in heaven and on earth and under the earth,
and every tongue confess that Jesus Christ is Lord,
to the glory of God the Father.

Philippians 2:9-11

620 All my hope on God is founded

Words and Music: Joachim Neander
arr. Chris Mitchell

MEINE HOFFNUNG 88 87 67

1. All my hope on God is found-ed; he doth still my trust re-new,
me through change and chance he guid-eth, on-ly good and on-ly true.
God un-known, he a-lone calls my heart to be his own.

2. Pride of man and earthly glory,
   sword and crown betray his trust;
   what with care and toil he buildeth,
   tower and temple, fall to dust.
   But God's pow'r,
   hour by hour,
   is my temple and my tower.

3. God's great goodness aye endureth,
   deep his wisdom, passing thought:
   splendour, life, and light attend him,
   beauty springeth out of naught.
   Evermore
   from his store
   new-born worlds rise and adore.

4. Daily doth th'almighty giver
   bounteous gifts on us bestow;
   his desire our soul delighteth,
   pleasure lead us where we go.
   Love doth stand
   at his hand;
   joy doth wait on his command.

5. Still from man to God eternal
   sacrifice of praise be done,
   high above all praises praising
   for the gift of Christ his Son.
   Christ doth call
   one and all:
   ye who follow shall not fall.

621 All my life I'll praise you
(You alone)

Words and Music: Wayne and Libby Huirua

All my life I'll praise you. There's no o-ther like you. You a-lone are Lord, Lord Je-

- sus. All my life I'll praise you. There's no o-ther like you. You

a-lone are Lord, Lord Je - sus, Lord Je - sus. - sus.

1. Who con-trols the rush-ing of the migh-ty wind,
2. He is the one who holds the u - ni - verse,

who holds the pow - er of the seas?
the pow'r of life is in his hands.

Who by his word formed the hea - vens and the earth?
His strength is in me, help - ing me to do his will.

Al - migh - ty God, the Lord Je - sus is his name.
He is my Lord, in his pow - er I will stand.

You a - lone are Lord, you a - lone are Lord, you

a - lone are Lord, Lord Je - sus.

622 All praise, all honour

(All praise)

Words and Music: James Wright

Now to him who is able to do
immeasurably more than all we ask or imagine,
according to his power that is at work within us,
to him be glory in the church
and in Christ Jesus throughout all generations,
for ever and ever! Amen.

Ephesians 3:20-21

623 All that I am

(I offer my life)

Words and Music: Claire Cloninger and Don Moen

use it for your glo - ry; Lord, I of-fer my days to you, lift-ing my praise

to you, as a pleas-ing sac - ri - fice;

To verse 2   *Last time*

Lord, I of - fer you my life.   life.

To continue

life.   What can we give that you have not gi - ven; and

what do we have that is not al-rea-dy yours? All we pos-sess are these lives

we're liv - ing, and that's what we give to you, Lord.

D.S.

2. Things in the past, things yet unseen,
   wishes and dreams that are yet to come true;
   all of my hopes, all of my plans,
   my heart and my hands are lifted to you.

624 All that is within me   *(Sing of your great love)*

Words and Music: Darlene Zschech
arr. Richard Lewis

1. All that is with-in me, Lord, will bless your ho - ly name, I

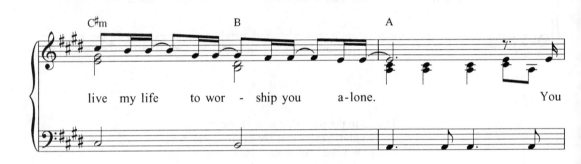

live my life to wor - ship you a-lone. You

brought me out of dark - ness and in - to your glo - rious light. For

e - ver I will sing of your great love, for

e - ver I will sing of your great love. 2. I

love to see you glo - ri-fied, to see you lift - ed high. I

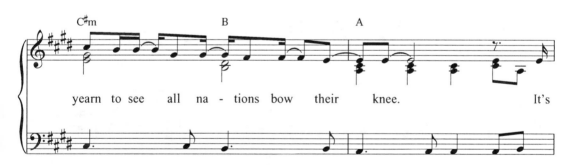

yearn to see all na - tions bow their knee. It's

you a-lone, Lord Je - sus, who can cause the cold - est heart to

3. And your trum - pet will sound, and

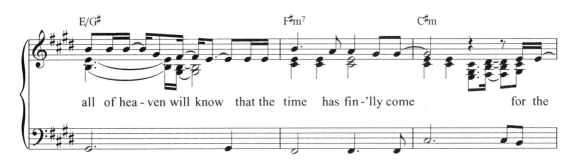

all of hea - ven will know that the time has fin -'lly come for the

bride to take her place and we'll hear the an - gels

D.S. al Coda CODA

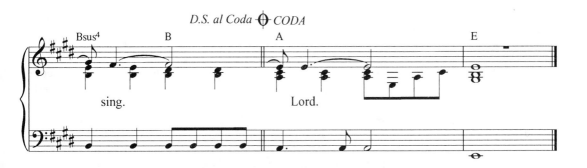

sing. Lord.

625 All the way

Words: Frances Jane van Alstyne (Fanny J. Crosby)

Music: Rich Mullins

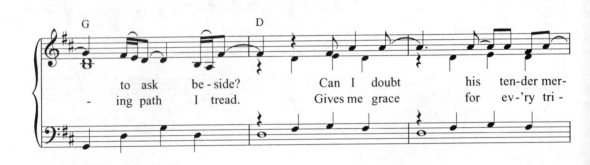

rest to me is pro - mised in my Fa - ther's house a - bove.

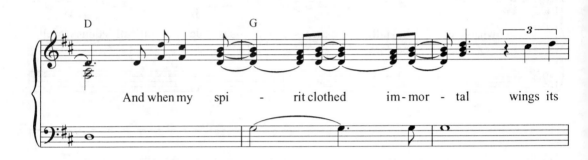

And when my spi - rit clothed im - mor - tal wings its

flight to realms of day, this my song through end-less a -

- ges, Je - sus led me all the way.

626 All the world can offer

(Because)

Words and Music: Colin Hardy
arr. Dave Bankhead

1. All the world can of-fer, none of it com-
2. All the world's wis-dom, chose to cru-ci-

pares with you. All the gold and sil-ver
fy the truth. But when you called I fol-lowed,

can't re-place the God I love. All the world sees
I have giv-en ev-'ry-thing for you. Je-sus, my

pre-cious, one day it will fade a-way,
trea-sure, you are my heart's de-sire.

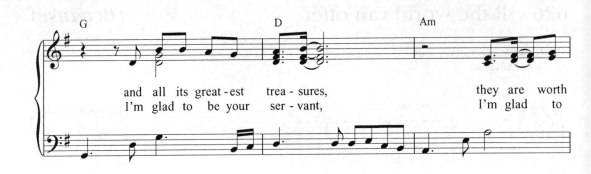

and all its great-est trea-sures,
I'm glad to be your ser-vant,

they are worth
I'm glad to

no-thing com-pared to you.
seek your king-dom first.

Be-cause you love me,

be-cause you called me,

be-cause you saved me I'm not liv-ing for this world,

'cause I'm liv - ing   for you.   Don't know   what I'd

do with-out your love,   don't know what I'd do with - out   you;

don't know   what I'd do with-out   your love,   your love   is the

on - ly ans - wer.   Don't know   what I'd

627 All who are thirsty

Words and Music: Brenton Brown and Glenn Robertson
arr. Chris Mitchell

The Lord will roar from Zion
and thunder from Jerusalem;
the earth and the sky will tremble.
But the Lord will be a refuge for his people,
a stronghold for the people of Israel.

Joel 3:16

628 All ye that pass by

Words: Charles Wesley

Music: William Knapp
arr. Chris Mitchell

WAREHAM LM

1. All ye that pass by, to Jesus draw nigh; to you is it nothing that Jesus should die? Your ransom and peace, your surety he is: come see if there ever was sorrow like his.

2. He dies to atone
   for sins not his own;
   your debt he hath paid,
   and your work he hath done.
   Ye all may receive
   the peace he did leave,
   who made intercession:
   my Father, forgive!

3. For you and for me
   he prayed on the tree:
   the pray'r is accepted,
   the sinner is free.
   That sinner am I,
   who on Jesus rely,
   and come for the pardon
   God cannot deny.

4. My pardon I claim;
   for a sinner I am,
   a sinner believing
   in Jesus's name.
   He purchased the grace
   which now I embrace:
   O Father, thou know'st
   he hath died in my place.

629 Almighty God

Words: *The Alternative Service Book* (1980)

Music: A. Piercy, D. Clifton
and C. Groves

Al - migh - ty God, to whom all hearts are o - pen,

all de - sires known, and from whom no se - crets are

hid - den: cleanse the thoughts of our

hearts by the in - spi - ra - tion of your Ho - ly

630 And here we are

(Here we are)

Words and Music: Claire Cloninger and Don Moen
arr. Chris Mitchell

You have al - ways been right be - side us, lead - ing us
It will be your strength that saves us, your love that

all a - long the way, and we've made it through,
makes us strong, and through it all,

be - cause of you.
we'll sing this song.

Chorus

And here we are

Praise him with the sounding of the trumpet,
praise him with the harp and lyre,
praise him with tambourine and dancing,
praise him with the strings and flute,
praise him with the clash of cymbals,
praise him with resounding cymbals.

Psalm 150:3-5

631 Angels from the realms of glory

Words: James Montgomery

Music: French or Flemish melody
arr. Richard Lloyd

IRIS 87 87 and Refrain

1. Angels from the realms of glory, wing your flight o'er all the earth;
ye who sang creation's story now proclaim Messiah's birth:

Chorus

Come and worship Christ, the new-born King; come

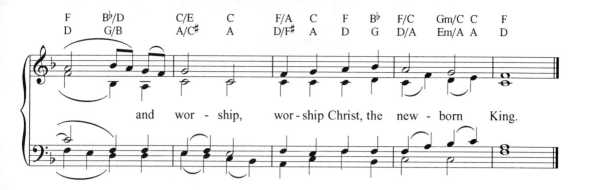

and wor - ship, wor - ship Christ, the new - born King.

2. Shepherds, in the field abiding,
   watching o'er your flocks by night,
   God with us is now residing,
   yonder shines the infant Light:

3. Sages, leave your contemplations;
   brighter visions beam afar:
   seek the great Desire of Nations;
   ye have seen his natal star:

4. Saints before the altar bending,
   watching long in hope and fear,
   suddenly the Lord, descending,
   in his temple shall appear:

5. Though an infant now we view him,
   he shall fill his Father's throne,
   gather all the nations to him;
   ev'ry knee shall then bow down:

Praise God in his sanctuary;
praise him in his mighty heavens.
Praise him for his acts of power;
praise him for his surpassing greatness.

Psalm 150:1-2

632 Approach, my soul, the mercy-seat

Words: John Newton

Music: Richard Farrant
arr. Chris Mitchell

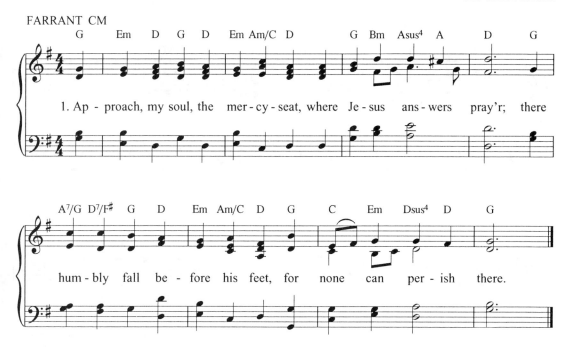

FARRANT CM

1. Ap-proach, my soul, the mer-cy-seat, where Je-sus ans-wers pray'r; there hum-bly fall be-fore his feet, for none can per-ish there.

2. Thy promise is my only plea,
   with this I venture nigh;
   thou callest burdened souls to thee
   and such, O Lord, am I!

3. Bowed down beneath the load of sin,
   by Satan sorely pressed,
   by wars without and fears within,
   I come to thee for rest.

4. Be thou my shield and hiding-place,
   that, sheltered near thy side,
   I may my fierce accuser face
   and tell him thou hast died.

5. O wondrous love! to bleed and die,
   to bear the cross and shame,
   that guilty sinners, such as I,
   might plead thy gracious name.

633 A rising generation *(In freedom)*

Words and Music: Aran Puddle

A peo-ple who are hun - gry,

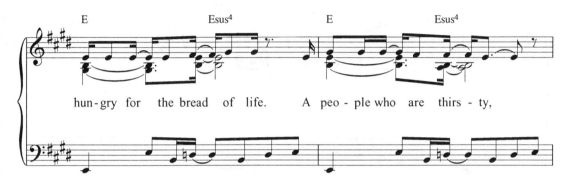

hun-gry for the bread of life. A peo-ple who are thirs-ty,

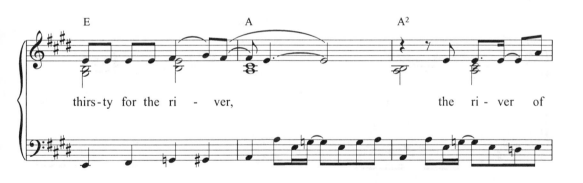

thirs-ty for the ri - ver, the ri - ver of

joy. And all a-cross this na - tion, a

634 As I come into your presence (*Precious Lord*)

Words and Music: Bill Drake
arr. Chris Mitchell

Not rushed

1. As I come in-to your pre - sence, and am moved with hum - ble rev-

- 'rence, I'm en - am - oured by the beau - ty of the

One who died to save me. I've been bought with blood as ran-

- som to be a child of your king - dom; I'm a

debt - or to your gos - pel, but an heir of ev - 'ry pro - mise. I will

2. When I come into your presence
   you will make my life a fragrance,
   I will see the One who's worthy,
   now displayed in awesome glory.
   I will hear the angels singing,
   see the nations humbly kneeling;
   clouds of witnesses surrounding,
   bring a symphony of praise!

635 As long as there is air to breathe

(I will give you praise)

Words and Music: David Klassen
arr. Chris Mitchell

1. As long as there is air to breathe, as long as there is life in me, while the

ri - ver runs in - to the sea I will give you praise. While the

rain-drops fall down from the sky and the sun-light beams down from on high, while the

li - on roars and birds can fly I will give you

2. As long as there is air to breathe,
   as long as there is life in me,
   while the river runs into the sea
   I will give you praise.
   And, though my days on earth will pass,
   the praise in me will always last;
   for however long forever lasts,
   I will give you praise.

636 As sure as gold is precious

(Revival)

Words and Music: Robin Mark

Verse

1. As sure as gold is pre-cious, and the
child out play-ing by their

ho - ney sweet,
own front door,

so you
ev - 'ry

love this ci - ty, and you love these streets.
ba - by ly - ing on the bed-room floor.

Ev-'ry

Chorus

I hear that thun-der in the

2. From the preacher preaching when the well is dry,
   to the lost soul reaching for a higher high.
   From the young man working through his hopes and fears,
   to the widow walking through the vale of tears.

3. Ev'ry man and woman, ev'ry old and young,
   ev'ry father's daughter, ev'ry mother's son;
   I feel it in my spirit, feel it in my bones,
   you're going to send revival, bring them all back home.

637 As the sun is reborn   *(Faithful God)*

Words and Music: David Baroni and Wayne Tate
arr.Chris Mitchell

As the sun is re-born, and a beau-ti-ful morn-ing re-minds
me of your faith-ful-ness to me. Through the
long, lone-ly night, when the dark-ness hid the light, you
gave me grace to trust and now I see. E-ven when it's
hard to be-lieve, e-ven when our hope seems all gone, there has

638 As we worship you

Words and Music: Tommy Walker
arr. Chris Mitchell

Verse

As we wor-ship you, let all the world come and see how the
wor-ship you, let all the na - tions hear our song, the song of

mer - cy we've re - ceived from you can set them free. As we
Je - sus and his blood that proved his love for all. As we

wor - ship you, let all this joy that fills our hearts bring a
wor - ship you, may all the lost and bro - ken come; may they

hun - ger and a hope to those who've strayed so far. As we
hear your still small voice call out their names, each one.

Chorus

639 As with gladness men of old

Words: William Chatterton Dix

Music: adapted from Conrad Kocher
by William Henry Monk

DIX 77 77 77

1. As with glad-ness men of old did the guid-ing star be-hold,
as with joy they hailed its light, lead-ing on-ward, beam-ing bright;
so, most gra-cious Lord, may we e-ver-more be led to thee.

2. As with joyful steps they sped,
   to that lowly manger-bed,
   there to bend the knee before
   him whom heav'n and earth adore,
   so may we with willing feet
   ever seek thy mercy-seat.

3. As their precious gifts they laid,
   at thy manger roughly made,
   so may we with holy joy,
   pure, and free from sin's alloy,
   all our costliest treasures bring,
   Christ, to thee our heav'nly King.

4. Holy Jesu, ev'ry day
   keep us in the narrow way;
   and, when earthly things are past,
   bring our ransomed souls at last
   where they need no star to guide,
   where no clouds thy glory hide.

5. In the heav'nly country bright
   need they no created light,
   thou its light, its joy, its crown,
   thou its sun which goes not down;
   there for ever may we sing
   alleluias to our King.

640 Beautiful Lord, wonderful Saviour
(The Potter's hand)

Words and Music: Darlene Zschech

teach me, dear Lord, to live all of my life through your

eyes. I'm cap-tured by your ho-ly call-ing,

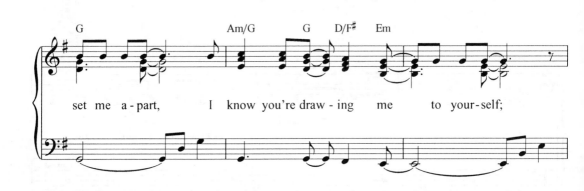

set me a-part, I know you're draw-ing me to your-self;

lead me, Lord, I pray.

641 Beauty for ashes

Words and Music: Neil Bennetts
arr. Chris Mitchell

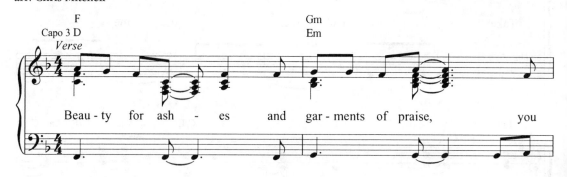

Beau-ty for ash - es and gar-ments of praise, you

come and a-dorn me with joy once a-gain, and

pour oil of glad - ness in in-stead of des-pair;

bring-ing your mer - cy a-gain like sweet, spring rain.

Let the name of the Lord be praised,
both now and for evermore.
From the rising of the sun to the place where it sets,
the name of the Lord is to be praised.

Psalm 113:2-3

642 Because of who he is

Words and Music: Capt. Alan Price, CA

1. Be-cause of who he is, be-cause of who he is,
be-cause of all he's done, be-cause of all he's done,
be-cause of all his love for us,
we wor-ship the Three in One.

2. We have come to God the Father,
we have come to God the Father,
in the name of God the Son,
in the name of God the Son,
by the power of the Spirit,
we worship the Three in One.

3. Because of who you are,
because of who you are,
because of all you've done,
because of all you've done,
because of all your love for us,
we worship the Three in One.

643 Before the throne of God above

Words: Charitie L. Bancroft

Music: Vikki Cook

1. Be-fore the throne of God a-bove I have a strong, a per-fect plea, a great High Priest whose name is Love, who-e-ver lives and pleads for me. My name is gra-ven on his hands, my name is writ-ten on his heart; I know that while in heav'n he stands no tongue can

bid me thence de - part, no tongue can bid me thence de - part.

2. When Satan tempts me to despair,
   and tells me of the guilt within,
   upward I look and see him there,
   who made an end to all my sin.
   Because the sinless Saviour died,
   my sinful soul is counted free;
   for God the Just is satisfied
   to look on him and pardon me,
   to look on him and pardon me.

3. Behold him there! The risen Lamb,
   my perfect, spotless righteousness;
   the great unchangeable I Am,
   the King of glory and of grace!
   One with himself I cannot die,
   my soul is purchased with his blood;
   my life is hid with Christ on high,
   with Christ, my Saviour and my God,
   with Christ, my Saviour and my God.

644 Behold the Lamb

Words and Music: Mark Altrogge

1. Be-hold the Lamb, sil-ent be-fore his ac-cu-sers as thorns are pressed in-to his brow. They lift him up, oh see the spikes that hold him, re-deem-ing blood flows down.

2. Be-hold the Lamb, car-ry-ing all our trans-gres-sions, he free-ly takes our place; en-dures the lash, the mock-ing and the laugh-ter of those he dies to save.

645 Better by far

Words and Music: Mark Altrogge

Better by far is your presence. Better by far is your Spirit. Nothing compares to your love poured out in my heart. Better by far poured out in my heart, it's better by far.

2. Better by far just to know you
   than be blessed in all other ways.
   Better by far that you work in my life
   to the praise of your glory and grace.

Praise the Lord, you his angels,
you mighty ones who do his bidding,
who obey his word.
Praise the Lord, all his heavenly hosts,
you his servants who do his will.
Praise the Lord, all his works
everywhere in his dominion.

Psalm 103:20-22

646 Blessed are the humble   *(The beatitudes)*

Words and Music: Graham Kendrick
arr. Richard Lewis

1. Blessed are   the hum-ble   in spi - rit,
   blessed are   those who hun-ger, who thirst for

jus - tice,   for theirs is   the King-dom   of
                   for sure-ly   you'll fill them   com-

hea - ven.   And blessed are   the
plet - ely.   And those who   show

647 Blessèd be the name of the Lord

Words and Music: Don Moen
arr. Chris Mitchell

Bles - sed be the name of the Lord, he is
wor - thy to be praised and a - dored; so we
lift up ho - ly hands in one ac - cord, sing - ing,
'Bles - sed be the name, bles - sed be the name,
bles - sed be the name of the Lord!'

648 Bless the Lord, O my soul

Words: Psalm 103:1

Music: unknown
arr. Chris Mitchell

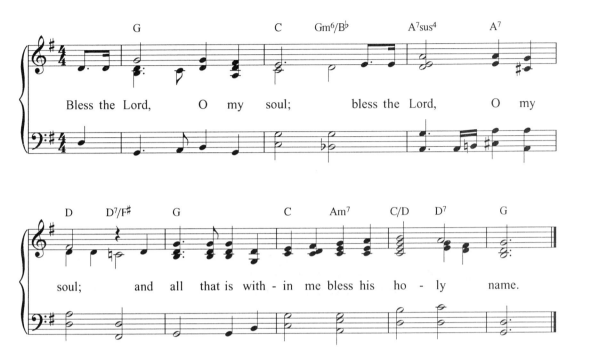

Bless the Lord, O my soul; bless the Lord, O my soul; and all that is with-in me bless his ho-ly name.

For the Lord is good and his love endures for ever;
his faithfulness continues through all generations.

Psalm 100:5

649 Bless the Lord, O my soul *(Bless his holy name)*

Words and Music: Andraé Crouch

650 Break the fallow ground *(I draw near)*

Words and Music: Loulita Di Somma
arr. Chris Mitchell

1. Break the fal-low ground in my hard-ened heart,
2. Lord, con-sume my soul, take my life, it's yours,

soft-en me a-gain;
breathe on me a-gain;

take me to the place, where I know your love,
in the sec-ret place, where I feel your touch,

Fa - ther, I draw near.
Fa - ther, I

I will proclaim the name of the Lord.
Oh, praise the greatness of our God!
He is the Rock, his works are perfect,
and all his ways are just.
A faithful God who does no wrong,
upright and just is he.

Deuteronomy 32:3-4

651 Breathe upon me

Words and Music: Henry Hinn
arr. Chris Mitchell

Breathe up-on me, breath of God, breathe up-on me, Spi-rit of the
Lord, as I lift my hands in sur-ren-der to your name, Most
High. Yield-ing to your Spi-rit, walk-ing in your
grace, Je-sus, I a-dore, Je-sus, I a-
dore, Je-sus, I a-dore your ho-ly name.

652 Christ above me

Words and Music: John Chisum and George Searcy

(♩ = 80)

Chorus

Christ a-bove me, Christ be-side me, Christ with-in me e-ver-guid-ing; Christ be-hind me, Christ be-fore, Christ, my love, my life, my Lord.

Verse

1. Bread of life from hea-ven, lo-ver of my

soul;   peace   of God   so   e - ver - pre - sent,

I   sur - ren - der   my con - trol   to   mind   to

2. Mercy everlasting,
   tenderness divine;
   word of God so ever-healing,
   I surrender heart and mind to

   Christ above me...

653 Christians, awake!

Words: John Byrom, alt.

Music: John Wainwright

YORKSHIRE (STOCKPORT) 10 10 10 10 10 10

1. Christ - ians, a - wake! Sa - lute the hap - py morn,

where - on the Sa - viour of the world was born;

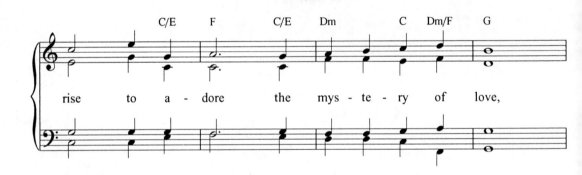

rise to a - dore the mys - te - ry of love,

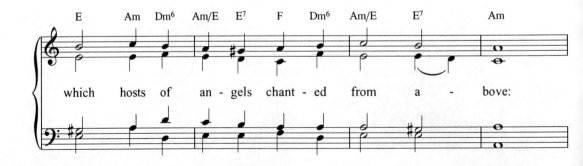

which hosts of an - gels chant - ed from a - bove:

with them the joy - ful ti - dings first be - gun of
God in - car - nate and the Vir - gin's Son.

2. Then to the watchful shepherds it was told,
who heard th'angelic herald's voice, 'Behold,
I bring good tidings of a Saviour's birth
to you and all the nations on the earth:
this day hath God fulfilled his promised word,
this day is born a Saviour, Christ the Lord.'

3. He spake; and straightway the celestial choir
in hymns of joy, unknown before, conspire;
the praises of redeeming love they sang,
and heav'n's whole orb with alleluias rang:
God's highest glory was their anthem still,
peace on the earth, in ev'ry heart good will.

4. To Bethl'em straight th'enlightened shepherds ran,
to see, unfolding, God's eternal plan,
and found, with Joseph and the blessèd maid,
her Son, the Saviour, in a manger laid:
then to their flocks, still praising God, return,
and their glad hearts with holy rapture burn.

5. O may we keep and ponder in our mind
God's wondrous love in saving lost mankind;
trace we the babe, who hath retrieved our loss,
from his poor manger to his bitter cross;
tread in his steps, assisted by his grace,
till our first heav'nly state again takes place.

6. Then may we hope, th'angelic hosts among,
to sing, redeemed, a glad triumphal song:
he that was born upon this joyful day
around us all his glory shall display;
saved by his love, incessant we shall sing
eternal praise to heav'n's almighty King.

654 Christ is made the sure foundation

Words: *Urbs Beata Jerusalem*
trans. John Mason Neale

Music: Henry Purcell
arr. E. Hawkins

WESTMINSTER ABBEY 87 87 87

1. Christ is made the sure foun-da-tion, Christ the head and
cor-ner-stone, cho-sen of the Lord, and pre-cious,
bind-ing all the Church in one, ho-ly Zi-on's
help for e-ver, and her con-fi-dence a-lone.

2. To this temple, where we call you,
come, O Lord of hosts, today;
you have promised loving kindness,
hear your servants as we pray,
bless your people now before you,
turn our darkness into day.

3. Hear the cry of all your people,
what they ask and hope to gain;
what they gain from you, for ever
with your chosen to retain,
and hereafter in your glory
evermore with you to reign.

4. Praise and honour to the Father,
praise and honour to the Son,
praise and honour to the Spirit,
ever Three and ever One,
One in might and One in glory,
while unending ages run.

655 Christ triumphant

Words: Michael Saward

Music: Michael Baughen

CHRIST TRIUMPHANT 85 85 and Refrain

1. Christ tri-um-phant, e-ver-reign-ing, Sa-viour, Mas-ter, King.

Lord of heav'n, our lives sus-tain-ing, hear us as we sing:

Chorus

Yours the glo-ry and the crown, the high re-nown, the e-ter-nal name.

2. Word incarnate, truth revealing,
   Son of Man on earth!
   Pow'r and majesty concealing
   by your humble birth:

3. Suff'ring servant, scorned, ill-treated,
   victim crucified!
   Death is through the cross defeated,
   sinners justified:

4. Priestly King, enthroned for ever
   high in heav'n above!
   Sin and death and hell shall never
   stifle hymns of love:

5. So, our hearts and voices raising
   through the ages long,
   ceaselessly upon you gazing,
   this shall be our song:

656 Christ, your glory

Words and Music: Steve James

Christ, your glory fills the heavens, your truth the world must know;
Morning Star, you triumph over darkness — you are Jesus the
Lord.

1. You are the sun of righteousness dawning that shall cause our hearts to sing; faithless shadows bringing healing in your wings.
2. You are the final word to be given, you're the hope that sets us free; let the earth be filled with your glory as the waters fill the sea!

Ascribe to the Lord the glory due to his name;
bring an offering and come into his courts.
Worship the Lord in the splendour of his holiness;
tremble before him, all the earth.

Psalm 96:8-9

657 Clothed with splendour and majesty

(Awesome God)

Words and Music: Andrew Bromley
arr. Chris Mitchell

Clothed with splen - dour and ma - jes - ty, you wear light like a robe, you

stretch out the hea - vens like a cur - tain, awe - some

God. You laid the earth on its foun-

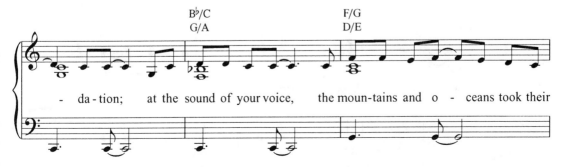

- da - tion; at the sound of your voice, the moun-tains and o - ceans took their

pla - ces, awe - some God.

Bridge

All the earth dis - plays your glo - ry, all cre - a - tion calls

your name. As all of hea - ven is stand - ing in awe,

all the na - tions shout your praise.

Cre - a - tion's an - them will rise to you, all the u - ni - verse

is cry-ing out for you, in a - do - ra - tion to the Ho - ly One,

in high - er prais - es to the awe - some God.

658 Come, let's lift our praise

(Lift our praise)

Words and Music: Geoff Bullock
arr. Dave Bankhead

Come, let's lift our praise, Lord, to you our song we raise, we will shout and sing with joy to you our God.

For you are our com - ing King, let us raise our voice and sing, Lord, we mag - ni - fy your name on high.

1. How good it is to praise and sing, with thanks-
giv-ing we lift our hearts. All the heav'ns a-bove will declare his love and his e-ne-mies will de - part.

2. Let us praise his name,
   people now proclaim
   his victorious majesty.
   Shout your praises high,
   all the earth and sky.
   Joy that lasts for eternity.

659 Come, let us rejoice before him *(Let us rejoice)*

Words and Music: Danny Antill
arr. Chris Mitchell

1. Come, let us re-joice be-fore him and make a joy-ful noise.

Come, let us bow down be-fore him and sing a song of praise! Ho-

san-na! You are glo-ri-ous. Ho-san-na! You are right-

-eous-ness. Ho-san-na! You're vic-to-ri-ous, Lord, we thank

you for your name. Ho-

2. Come, let us proclaim his greatness,
   he healed the blind and lame.
   He is the Lord and Saviour
   and Jesus is his name.

3. Come, let us dance before him
   and bless his holy name.
   He is the first and last
   and he always stays the same!

660 Come, let us sing

Words: Robert Walmsley

Music: F.L. Wiseman

WONDERFUL LOVE 10 4 10 7 4 10

1. Come, let us sing of a won-der-ful love, ten-der and true; out of the heart of the Fa-ther a-bove, stream-ing to me and to you: won-der-ful love dwells in the heart of the Fa-ther a-bove.

2. Jesus, the Saviour, this gospel to tell,
joyfully came;
came with the helpless and hopeless to dwell,
sharing their sorrow and shame;
seeking the lost,
saving, redeeming at measureless cost.

3. Jesus is seeking the wanderers yet;
why do they roam?
Love only waits to forgive and forget;
home! weary wanderer, home!
Wonderful love
dwells in the heart of the Father above.

4. Come to my heart, O thou wonderful love,
come and abide,
lifting my life till it rises above
envy and falsehood and pride;
seeking to be
lowly and humble, a learner of thee.

661 Come, let us worship and bow down

Words and Music: Dave Doherty
arr. Chris Mitchell

662 Come, now is the time to worship

Words and Music: Brian Doerksen

Sing to the Lord a new song;
sing to the Lord, all the earth.
Sing to the Lord, praise his name;
proclaim his salvation day after day.
Declare his glory among the nations,
his marvellous deeds among all peoples.

Psalm 96:1-3

663 Come, thou fount of every blessing

Words and Music: Robert Robinson
arr. Chris Mitchell

1. Come, thou fount of ev-'ry bles - sing, tune my heart to sing thy grace; streams of mer - cy, ne - ver ceas - ing, call for songs of loud - est praise. Teach me some me - lo-dious son - net, sung by flam - ing tongues a - bove; praise the mount, I'm fixed up - on it, mount of thy re-deem-ing love.

2. O to grace, how great a debtor,
   daily I'm constrained to be,
   let thy grace, Lord, like a fetter,
   bind my wand'ring heart to thee.
   Prone to wander, Lord, I feel it,
   prone to leave the God I love;
   here's my heart, Lord, take and seal it;
   seal it for thy courts above.

664 Come to me, Lord
(More of you, Lord)

Words and Music: Eric Nuzum and Chris Springer
arr. Chris Mitchell

Come to me, Lord (come to me,

Lord), here is my heart (here is my

heart); can't live on my own (can't live on my

own), can't live with-out you. I want

665 Come to the power   *(A mighty fortress)*

Words and Music: Richard Lewis

With energy - reggae feel in refrain

Come to the pow-er, the pow-er of the liv-ing God.

His name is high-er, high-er than a - ny o - ther name:

migh - ty Je - ho-vah, awe - some de - li - ver - er,

his pow'r is great-er, great-er that a - ny prin-ci-pa-li -

ty. A migh - ty fort - ress is our God;

666 Come worship, come bow down

Words and Music: Arthur Tannous
arr. Chris Mitchell

Come wor-ship, come bow down, in rev-'rence to him crowned our Sa-viour, who en-com-passed all fa-vour and com-pas-sion. Wor-ship his ten-der love and mer-cy, wor-ship his ho-li-ness. Wor-ship his grace and

667 Come, ye sinners, poor and needy *(I will arise)*

Words: Joseph Hart

Music: Ingrid DuMosch and Calvin Bottoms

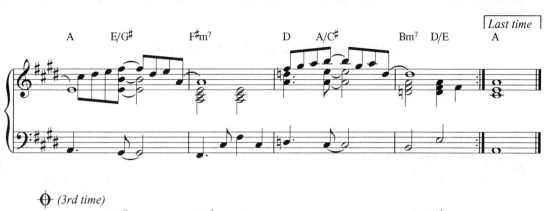

A E/G♯ F♯m⁷ D A/C♯ Bm⁷ D/E A

(3rd time)

A E/G♯ D/F♯ D/E D A/C♯

Come, ye wea-ry, hea-vy-la-den, lost and

Bm⁷ D/E A Bm⁷ C

ru-ined by the fall; if you tar-ry till you're be-

G/B Am⁷ B⁷sus⁴ B⁷ *Chorus* D.S.

-ter, you will ne-ver come at all. I will a-rise

2. Come, ye thirsty, come and welcome,
   God's free bounty glorify;
   true belief and true repentance,
   ev'ry grace that brings you nigh.

3. Let not conscience make you linger,
   nor of fitness fondly dream;
   all the fitness he requireth,
   is to feel you need of him.

668 Could I bring you words of comfort
(What Jesus would have done)

Words and Music: David Clifton
and Phil Baggaley arr. Chris Mitchell

1. Could I bring you words of com - fort, of - fer peace where there is war? Could I bless the ones who curse me, can I for - give the ones who hurt me most? Lord, I will, so hear my prayer.

Let your Spi - rit lead me on

to where I stand with the bro - ken, it's what Je -

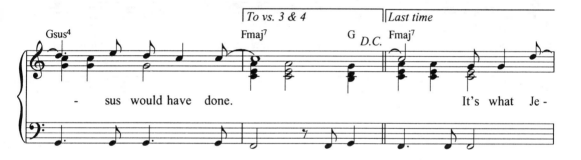

To vs. 3 & 4 | *Last time*

- sus would have done. It's what Je -

- sus would have done, it's what Je - sus would have done.

2. Would I weep if you were weeping,
   walk with those the world disowns?
   Can I break the bread of heaven
   with ev'ry lost, lost and hungry soul?

3. Would I stand against injustice,
   speak for those who cannot speak?
   Be the hands that help the helpless,
   and be your arms, the arms that hold the weak?

4. Could I lose the life you gave me,
   lay it down with all I own?
   Will I walk with ev'ry pilgrim
   who walks this road, this narrow way of love?

669 Create in me a clean heart

Words and Music: Keith Green

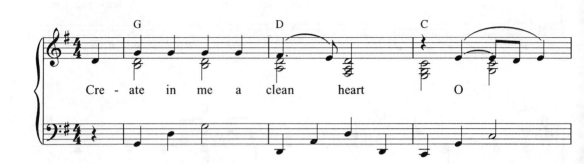

Cre - ate in me a clean heart O

God, and re-new a right spi - rit with-in

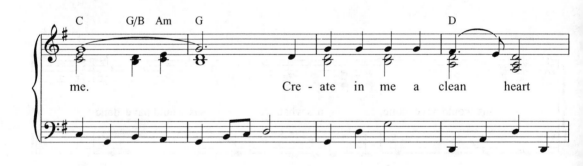

me. Cre - ate in me a clean heart

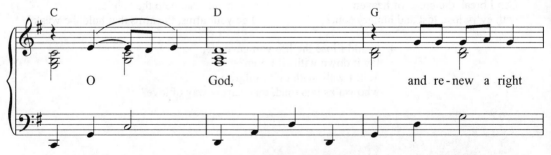

O God, and re-new a right

How lovely is your dwelling-place,
O Lord Almighty!
My soul yearns, even faints,
for the courts of the Lord;
my heart and my flesh cry out
for the living God.

Psalm 84:1-2

670 Create in me a pure heart

Words and Music: Sue Howson

1. Cre-ate in me a pure heart that's yours for e-ver, yield-ed and stead-fast, se-cure in your love. Re-store to me joy in be-long-ing to you. Make me yours, Lord, make me yours, I long to be de-vo-ted to you.

2. Oh may my life be one that's willing to live for you,
   bearing the marks of sacrifice,
   living to die, laying all down for your name.
   Make me yours, Lord, make me yours,
   I long to be devoted to you.

671 Creation is awaiting

Words and Music: Chris Bowater and Ian Taylor

2. The church is awaiting the return of the King.
   The people joined together in his love.
   Redeemed by his blood,
   washed in his word.
   As a bride longs for her bridegroom
   the church looks to God.
Chorus:
   The King is coming, the King is coming,
   the King is coming to receive his bride. *(x2)*

3. The world is awaiting the return of the King.
   The earth is a footstool for his feet.
   Ev'ry knee will bow down,
   ev'ry tongue confess,
   that Jesus Christ is Lord
   of heaven and earth.
Chorus:
   The King is coming, the King is coming,
   the King is coming to reign in majesty. *(x2)*

I will praise you, O Lord, among the nations;
I will sing of you among the peoples.
For great is your love, reaching to the heavens;
your faithfulness reaches to the skies.
Be exalted, O God, above the heavens;
let your glory be over all the earth.

Psalm 57:9-11

672 Crown him King of kings

Words and Music: Sharon Damazio

673 Deep within my heart *(You are the one)*

Words and Music: Simon Goodall

1. Deep with-in my heart is a long - ing to know you more. I have searched for love un-end - ing and have found you to be true. You are the one that I live for, there's no one else that I love more;

you're all I need, my all in all, and I a-

dore you, I a - dore you, Lord.

2. Once we were apart
   then you found me
   and made me your own.
   All this world had to offer
   couldn't match the love you've shown.

674 Draw me close to you

Words and Music: Kelly Carpenter

Draw me close to you, ne-ver let me go.
You are my de-sire, no one else will do,

I lay it all down a-gain,
'cause no-thing else could take your place,

to hear you say that I'm your friend.
to feel the warmth of your em-brace.

Help me find the way, bring me back to you.

God has ascended amid shouts of joy,
the Lord amid the sounding of trumpets.
Sing praises to God, sing praises;
sing praises to our King, sing praises.
For God is the King of all the earth;
sing to him a psalm of praise.

Psalm 47:5-7

675 Emmanuel

Words and Music: Bob McGee
arr. Chris Mitchell

676 Empty, broken, here I stand

(Kyrie eleison)

Words and Music: Nick and Anita Haigh
arr. Chris Mitchell

son. Ky - ri - e   e - lei - son, Chris - te

e - lei - son, Ky - ri - e   e - lei - son.

Last time Fine   D.C.

2. When my faith has all but gone,
   Kyrie eleison,
   give me strength to carry on,
   Kyrie eleison.
   When my dreams have turned to dust,
   Kyrie eleison,
   in you, O Lord, I put my trust,
   Kyrie eleison.

3. When my heart is cold as ice,
   your love speaks of sacrifice,
   love that sets the captive free,
   O pour compassion down on me.

4. You're the voice that calms my fears,
   you're the laughter, dries my tears,
   you're my music, my refrain,
   help me sing your song again.

5. Humble heart of holiness,
   kiss me with your tenderness,
   Jesus, faithful friend and true,
   all I am I give to you.

Clap your hands, all you nations;
shout to God with cries of joy.
How awesome is the Lord Most High,
the great King over all the earth!

Psalm 47:1-2

677 Eternal light, eternal light!

Words: Thomas Binney

Music: Henry L. Morley

NEWCASTLE 86 88 6

1. E-ter-nal light, e-ter-nal light! how pure the soul must be, when, placed with-in thy search-ing sight, it shrinks not, but with calm de-light, can live and look on thee.

2. The spirits that surround thy throne
   may bear that burning bliss;
   but that is surely theirs alone,
   since they have never, never known
   a fallen world like this.

3. O how shall I, whose native sphere
   is dark, whose mind is dim,
   before th'Ineffable appear,
   and on my naked spirit bear
   the uncreated beam?

4. There is a way for us to rise
   to that sublime abode;
   an off'ring and a sacrifice,
   a Holy Spirit's energies,
   an Advocate with God.

5. These, these prepare us for the sight
   of holiness above;
   the sons of ignorance and night
   can dwell in the eternal light,
   through the eternal love.

678 Everybody everywhere

Words and Music: Graham Kendrick
arr. Richard Lewis

Ev-'ry-bo-dy ev-'ry-where,

bless his ho-ly name. Ev-'ry-bo-dy ev-'ry-where,

for e - ver. Ev-'ry-bo-dy ev-'ry-where,

sing a-bout his love. Ev-'ry-bo-dy ev-'ry-where,

awe   and tell their child – ren what he's done.
name   tell – ing the glo – ries of your reign.

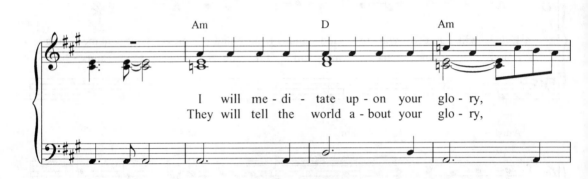

I will me – di – tate up – on your glo – ry,
They will tell the world a – bout your glo – ry,

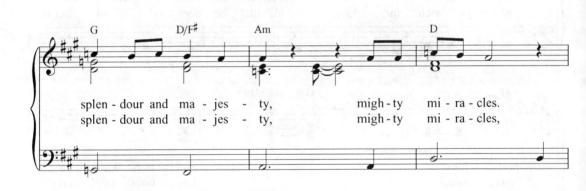

splen – dour and ma – jes – ty,   migh – ty mi – ra – cles.
splen – dour and ma – jes – ty,   migh – ty mi – ra – cles,

Let them be on ev – 'ry tongue,   tell the glo – rious things you've done.
and this glo-rious King shall reign   ge – ne – ra – tions with – out end.

Ev-'ry-bo-dy ev-ry-where, for e - ver and e - ver,

for e - ver and e - ver.

679 Everything I am

Words and Music: Ian Mizen and Andy Pressdee
arr. Richard Lewis

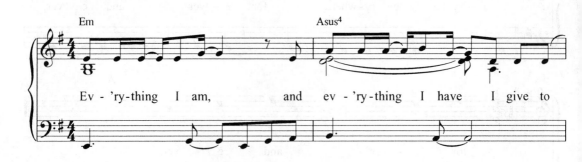

Ev - 'ry-thing I am, and ev - 'ry-thing I have I give to

you.

Ev - 'ry-thing I want, and ev - 'ry-thing I dream I give to

you. You are,

680 Fairest Lord Jesus

Words: Lilian Stevenson
from the German

Music: from *Silesian Folk Songs*

SCHÖNSTER HERR JESU 568 558

1. Fair - est Lord Je - sus; rul - er of all na - ture, O thou of
God and man the Son; thee will I che - rish, thee will I
hon - our, thou my soul's glo - ry, joy, and crown.

2. Fair are the meadows;
   fairer still the woodlands,
   robed in the blooming garb of spring.
   Jesus is fairer,
   Jesus is purer;
   who makes the woeful heart to sing.

3. Fair is the sunshine;
   fairer still the moonlight
   and all the twinkling starry host.
   Jesus shines brighter,
   Jesus shines purer;
   than all the angels heav'n can boast.

4. Beautiful Saviour!
   Lord of the nations!
   Son of God and Son of Man!
   Glory and honour,
   praise, adoration,
   now and for evermore be thine!

Who may ascend the hill of the Lord?
Who may stand in his holy place?
He who has clean hands and a pure heart,
who does not lift up his soul to an idol
or swear by what is false.

Psalm 24:3-4

681 Faithful are your mercies, Lord
(Great is your faithfulness)

Words and Music: Mark Altrogge
arr. Dave Bankhead

1. Faith-ful are your mer-cies, Lord, they drench me like the dew.
   seat me at your ta-ble, Lord, you've gi-ven me a place.

Pure and sweet your ho-ly love; I
You robe me in your right-eous-ness, a-

find my joy in you. Your fa-vour greets me like
dorn-ing me with grace. You crown me with your vic-

the dawn, my burn-ing heart must sing to
-tor's wreath you gained up-on the tree. You

682 Father, to you

(What grace)

Words and Music: Graham Kendrick
arr. Richard Lewis

1. Fa - ther, to you with songs of love we come in - to your pre - sence in awe of all you've done, brought here with joy be - fore your throne of grace and in the Son you love giv - en our place.

What grace to be found in him, hea - ven's glo - rious King. Fa - ther, what grace! Rais - ing us to

2. Deep is the joy that fills your courts above,
   while angels wonder at your redeeming love;
   and, as you gaze with joy upon your Son,
   your eyes are on the ones his love has won.

3. No higher call than to be heirs with him,
   so let our passion burn for heavenly things.
   Seated with Christ, for him alone to live,
   our hearts for ever where our treasure is.

O Lord, our Lord,
how majestic is your name in all the earth!
You have set your glory
above the heavens.

Psalm 8:1

683 Fill thou my life, O Lord, my God

Words: Horatius Bonar, alt.

Music: melody adapted from Thomas Haweis

RICHMOND CM

1. Fill thou my life, O Lord, my God, in ev-'ry part with praise, that my whole be-ing may pro-claim thy be-ing and thy ways.

2. Not for the lip of praise alone,
   nor e'en the praising heart,
   I ask, but for a life made up
   of praise in ev'ry part.

3. Praise in the common things of life,
   its goings out and in;
   praise in each duty and each deed,
   however small and mean.

4. Fill ev'ry part of me with praise;
   let all my being speak
   of thee and of thy love, O Lord,
   poor though I be and weak.

5. So shalt thou, Lord, receive from me
   the praise and glory due;
   and so shall I begin on earth
   the song for ever new.

6. So shall each fear, each fret, each care,
   be turnèd into song;
   and ev'ry winding of the way
   the echo shall prolong.

7. So shall no part of day or night
   unblest or common be;
   but all my life, in ev'ry step,
   be fellowship with thee.

684 For all the saints

Words: William Walsham How

Music: Ralph Vaughan Williams

The eternal God is your refuge,
and underneath are the everlasting arms.
He will drive out your enemy before you,
saying, 'Destroy him!'

Deuteronomy 33:27

685 For the fruits of his creation

Words: Fred Pratt Green

Music: traditional Welsh melody
arr. Colin Hand

AR HYD Y NOS 84 84 88 84

1. For the fruits of his cre-a-tion, thanks be to God;
for his gifts to ev-'ry na-tion, thanks be to God;
for the plough-ing, sow-ing, reap-ing, sil-ent growth while we are sleep-ing,
fu-ture needs in earth's safe-keep-ing, thanks be to God.

2. In the just reward of labour,
   God's will is done;
   in the help we give our neighbour,
   God's will is done;
   in our world-wide task of caring
   for the hungry and despairing,
   in the harvests we are sharing,
   God's will is done.

3. For the harvests of his Spirit,
   thanks be to God;
   for the good we all inherit,
   thanks be to God;
   for the wonders that astound us,
   for the truths that still confound us,
   most of all, that love has found us,
   thanks be to God.

686 Freedom and liberty

Words and Music: Michael Battersby

Free - dom and lib - er - ty, now I got a rev - e - la - tion what you did for me. You broke the chains and you set me free and I'm ne-

- ver go - ing back a - gain. You're my strong

and migh - ty for - tress, you're my shel - ter.

687 Friend of sinners

Words and Music: Matt Redman

1. Friend of sin-ners, Lord of truth, I am fall-ing in love with you. Friend of sin-ners, Lord of truth, I have fal-len in love with you. Je - sus, I love your name, the name by which we're saved. Je -

2. Friend of sin-ners, Lord of truth, I am giv-ing my life to you. Friend of sin-ners, Lord of truth, I have giv-en my life to you. Je - sus, I

688 Give thanks to the Lord

(For ever)

Words and Music: Chris Tomlin

Moderato

Verse

1. Give thanks to the Lord, our God and King:
2. With a migh-ty hand and out-stretched arm: his
3. From the ri - sing to the set - ting sun:

love en - dures for e - ver. For he is good, he is a -
For the life that's
By the grace of God, we will

bove all things:
been re - born: his love en - dures for e - ver. Sing
car - ry on:

Verse 1

praise, sing praise.

689 Give us passion for the Lamb of God
(Passion for Jesus)

Words and Music: Richard Lewis

690 Glorious Lord, wonderful King

Words and Music: Carol Mundy
arr. Chris Mitchell

Glo - ri - ous Lord, won - der - ful King of kings and Lord of

Glo - ry. Faith - ful and true, wor - thy are you of the

hon - our, glo - ry and praise. Migh - ty, ma - jes - tic, vic -

to - rious Lord. Je - sus, Sa - viour, the One we a - dore.

Faith - ful and true, wor-thy are you and we crown you

To repeat

Lord of all.

Last time

all, and we

crown you Lord of all.

691 Glorious things of thee are spoken

Words: John Newton
based on Isaiah 33:20-21, alt.

Music: Croatian folk melody
adapted by Franz Joseph Haydn

AUSTRIA 87 87 D

1. Glo - rious things of thee are spo - ken, Zi - on, ci - ty of our God;

he whose word can - not be bro - ken formed thee for his own a - bode.

On the Rock of A - ges found - ed, what can shake thy sure re - pose?

With sal - va - tion's walls sur - round - ed, thou may'st smile at all thy foes.

2. See, the streams of living waters,
   springing from eternal love,
   well supply thy sons and daughters,
   and all fear of want remove.
   Who can faint while such a river
   ever flows their thirst to assuage?
   Grace which, like the Lord, the giver,
   never fails from age to age.

3. Round each habitation hov'ring,
   see the cloud and fire appear
   for a glory and a cov'ring,
   showing that the Lord is near.
   Thus they march, the pillar leading,
   light by night and shade by day;
   daily on the manna feeding
   which he gives them when they pray.

4. Saviour, if of Zion's city
   I through grace a member am,
   let the world deride or pity,
   I will glory in thy name.
   Fading is the worldling's pleasure,
   boasted pomp and empty show;
   solid joys and lasting treasure
   none but Zion's children know.

692 Glory, glory, glory to the Lamb

Words and Music: Larry Dempsey
arr. Chris Mitchell

693 Glory, glory, I give you glory

(Blessing and honour)

Words and Music: D. Klassen
arr. Chris Mitchell

C   A/C#   Dm   C
A   F#/A#   Bm   A

                                                    Chorus

I'd ra - ther bow down to   but you.   Bles-sing and hon-

B♭maj⁷   C/B♭   B♭maj⁷
Gmaj⁷   A/G   Gmaj⁷

- our to   you, Lord,   you are the on - ly liv - ing God.
- 'ry o - ther name,   Je - sus, you al - ways will   re - main.

C/B♭   Gm⁷   1. A⁷
A/G   Em⁷   F#⁷

Wor-thy of all   the prai - ses flow - ing from my heart.
Hea-ven and earth will pass, but   you

C/D   Dm⁷   2. A⁷
A/B   Bm⁷   F#⁷

                              Name a - bove ev -   will stay   the same.

(Instrumental)

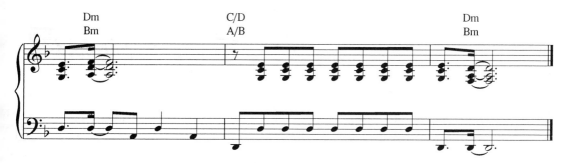

694 Glory, honour, power belongs to you

(We cry, 'Holy')

Words and Music: Scott Wesley Brown
arr. Richard Lewis

Glo-ry, hon-our, pow-er be-longs to you, Lord,

bless-ing, prais-es, wis-dom and strength are yours. We cry,

'Ho - ly, Lord, you are ho - ly', on - ly

you will we praise and a - dore. We cry,

'Wor - thy, Lord, you are wor - thy', for e - ver and e - ver, for

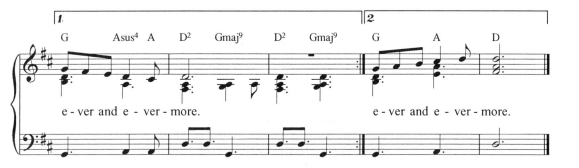

e - ver and e - ver - more.   e - ver and e - ver - more.

Shout for joy to the Lord, all the earth,
burst into jubilant song with music;
make music to the Lord with the harp,
with the harp and the sound of singing,
with trumpets and the blast of the ram's horn –
shout for joy before the Lord, the King.

Psalm 98:4-6

695 Glory to you

Words and Music: Scott Wesley Brown
arr. Richard Lewis

1. Glo - ry to you, glo - ry to you; may all that we are, and all that we do bring glo-ry, Lord, to you.
2. Hon - our to you, hon - our to you; may all that we are, and all that we do bring hon-our, Lord, to you.
3. Bless - ing to you, bless - ing to you; may all that we are, and all that we do bring bless-ing, Lord, to you.

696 God Almighty, let your presence

(Let your glory fall)

Words and Music: Michael Battersby

Lyrics:

God Al-migh-ty, let your pre-sence fill this place;

Lord, you're all I need and you're all that I long for.

My de-sire is to wor-ship you a-lone

in this se-cret place; let me dwell here for e-ver.

Rush-ing wind, con-sum-ing fire, fill this place,

697 God in the darkness   *(Beginning and end)*

**Words and Music: David Bird, Richard Lacy
and Sarah Lacy arr. Chris Mitchell**

2. God in the tiniest infinite detail,
   God in the nearest and furthest away,
   Lord of all heaven and earth's great Creator,
   God at beginning and end of the day,
   God at beginning and end of the day.

3. I lay down my fear and my hatred,
   tear down the curtain of sin;
   open my heart and let all that is good enter in.

4. God in the darkness and God in the morning,
   God in the work and the pain and the play,
   Lord of all heaven and earth's great Creator,
   God at beginning and end of the day,
   God at beginning and end of the day.

5. I lay down, my heart is so weary,
   and gaze on his presence with awe.
   There's nothing too small to entrust to the infinite God.

6. God for the humble and weak and bewildered,
   God for the nearest and furthest away,
   Lord of all heaven and earth's great Creator,
   God at beginning and end of the day,
   God at beginning and end of the day.

698 God is our refuge and our strength

Words and Music: David Clifton

God is our re-fuge and our strength, an e-ver-pre-sent help in times of trou-ble. The seas may rise up, the na - tions may fall, but there's a ci - ty, a ho - ly

699 God is our strength and refuge

Words: from Psalm 46, Richard Bewes

Music: Eric Coates, arr. John Barnard

DAM BUSTER'S MARCH 77 75 77 11

1. God is our strength and re-fuge, our pre-sent help in trou-ble, and we there-fore will not fear, though the earth should change! Though moun-tains shake and trem-ble, though swirl-ing wa-ters are rag-ing, God the Lord of hosts is with us e - ver - more!

2. There is a flowing river,
within God's holy city;
God is in the midst of her,
she shall not be moved!
God's help is swiftly given,
thrones vanish at his presence,
God the Lord of hosts is with us evermore!

3. Come, see the works of our maker,
learn of his deeds all-pow'rful;
wars will cease across the world
when he shatters the spear!
Be still and know your creator,
uplift him in the nations,
God the Lord of hosts is with us evermore!

700 God moves in a mysterious way

Words: William Cowper

Music: from the *Scottish Psalter*
adapted by John Playford

LONDON NEW CM

1. God moves in a my-ste-rious way his won-ders to per-form; he
plants his foot-steps in the sea, and rides up-on the storm.

2. Deep in unfathomable mines
   of never-failing skill,
   he treasures up his bright designs,
   and works his sov'reign will.

3. Ye fearful saints, fresh courage take;
   the clouds ye so much dread
   are big with mercy, and shall break
   in blessings on your head.

4. Judge not the Lord by feeble sense,
   but trust him for his grace;
   behind a frowning providence
   he hides a shining face.

5. His purposes will ripen fast,
   unfolding ev'ry hour;
   the bud may have a bitter taste,
   but sweet will be the flow'r.

6. Blind unbelief is sure to err,
   and scan his work in vain;
   God is his own interpreter,
   and he will make it plain.

701 God sent his Son   *(Because he lives)*

Words and Music: Gloria Gaither and William J. Gaither

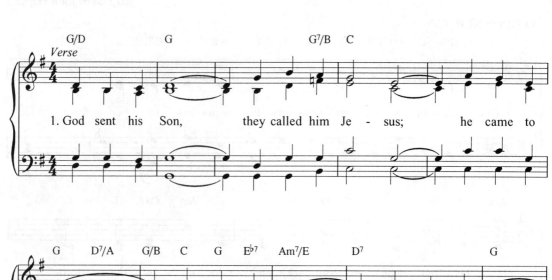

1. God sent his Son, they called him Je-sus; he came to

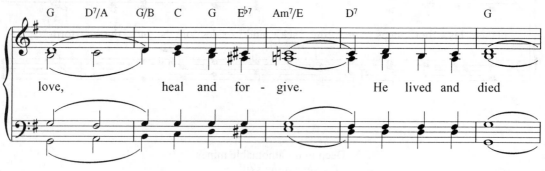

love, heal and for-give. He lived and died

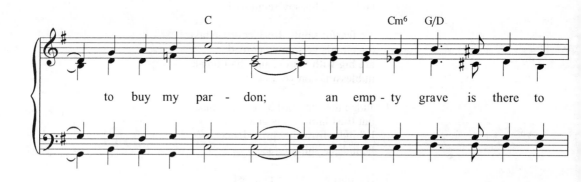

to buy my par-don; an emp-ty grave is there to

prove my Sa-viour lives. Be-cause he lives I can face to-

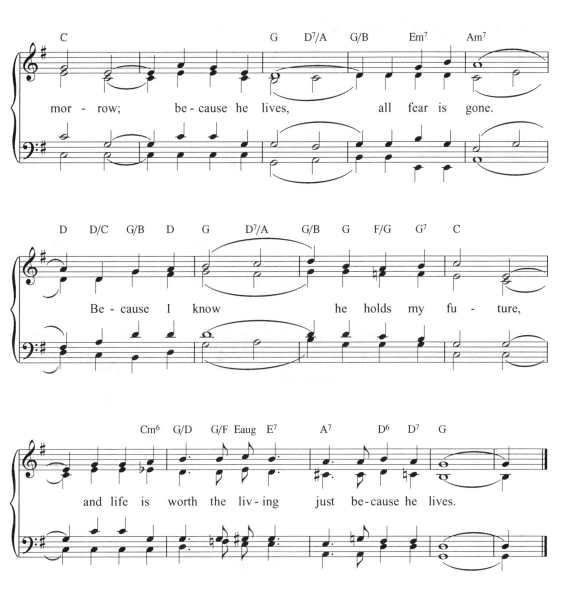

mor - row; be - cause he lives, all fear is gone.

Be - cause I know he holds my fu - ture,

and life is worth the liv - ing just be - cause he lives.

2. How sweet to hold a new-born baby,
   and feel the pride and joy he gives;
   but greater still the calm assurance:
   this child can face uncertain days because he lives.

3. And then one day I'll cross the river;
   I'll fight life's final war with pain.
   And then, as death gives way to vict'ry,
   I'll see the lights of glory and I'll know he reigns.

702 God, you keep us   *(For the glory of your name)*

Words and Music: John Hartley and Gary Sadler

1. God, you keep us with - out fall - ing, as you

watch us from a - bove; in our com - ings and our go -

- ings, shel - tered by your pre - cious love. In the

pour - ing rain of mer - cy comes the grace by which we're saved

for the glo - ry of your

name, for the glo - ry of your name.

2. You have touched our lives for ever,
   can we be the same again?
   May our hearts be ever faithful,
   ever faithful as a friend.
   Let us live that we may serve you,
   overflowing with your praise,
   for the glory of your name,
   for the glory of your name.

3. We behold the man of sorrows
   hanging there upon a cross,
   where we wounded one so holy,
   yet these wounds are life to us.
   For the blood you shed was perfect
   and your finished work remains
   for the glory of your name,
   for the glory of your name.

4. Now we lift our eyes to heaven,
   see you seated on the throne;
   still rejoicing in your promise,
   this is where our hope is found.
   For we know that you are coming,
   ev'ry tongue will sing your fame,
   for the glory of your name,
   for the glory of your name.

703 God, you're my God

Words and Music: Stuart Garrard
arr. Chris Mitchell

CODA

wor-thy. So I will praise you,

as long as I live. So I will

praise you, as long as I live.

Speak to one another
with psalms, hymns and spiritual songs.
Sing and make music in your heart to the Lord,
always giving thanks to God the Father for everything,
in the name of our Lord Jesus Christ.

Ephesians 5:19-20

704 Greater grace

Words and Music: Chris Bowater

1. Grea-ter grace, deep-er mer-cy, wi-der love, high-er
   hope, full as-sur-ance, joy that more than sat-is-

ways. Per-fect peace, com-plete for-give-ness, it's
fies. Com-fort, strength, pow'r and heal-ing,

all found in you, it's all found in you. 2. More than

you. It's all found in you, Je-sus, it's

705 Great is he who's the King of kings

Words and Music: unknown

Great is he who's the King of kings and the

Al - le - lu - ia, al - le - lu - ia, al - le-

Al - le - lu - ia, sal - va - tion and glo - ry,

C   C/E   F   Dm⁷   G   G/F   E⁷   E⁷/G♯

Lord of lords, he is won - der - ful!

lu - ia, he is won - der - ful!

hon - our and pow - er, he is won - der - ful!

Am   Am/C   Dm⁷   Gsus⁴   G   C

706 Great is the Lord

Words and Music: Michael W. Smith and Deborah D. Smith

707 Great, O Lord

Words and Music: David Hind
arr. Dave Bankhead

Great, O Lord is your ho-li-ness, is your

love-li-ness. Great, O Lord is your

ho-li-ness, is your love-li-ness; and I'll pro-claim

Je-sus is Lord, Je-sus is won-der-ful; the

Name a- bove all names. And I'll pro - claim Je - sus is

Lord, Je - sus is won-der-ful. Great is the

Lord; great is the Lord.

I will pour out my Spirit on all people.
Your sons and daughters will prophesy,
your old men will dream dreams,
your young men will see visions.
Even on my servants, both men and women,
I will pour out my Spirit in those days.

Joel 2:28, 29

708 Guide me, O thou great Jehovah

Words: William Williams trans. Peter Williams and others

Music: John Hughes

CWM RHONDDA 87 87 87

1. Guide me, O thou great Jehovah, pilgrim through this barren land; I am weak, but thou art mighty, hold me with thy pow'r-ful hand: Bread of heaven, Bread of heaven, feed me now and evermore, feed me now and evermore.

2. Open now the crystal fountain
   whence the healing stream doth flow;
   let the fiery, cloudy pillar
   lead me all my journey through:
   strong Deliverer, strong Deliverer,
   be thou still my strength and shield,
   be thou still my strength and shield.

3. When I tread the verge of Jordan
   bid my anxious fears subside;
   death of death, and hell's destruction,
   land me safe on Canaan's side:
   songs of praises, songs of praises,
   I will ever give to thee,
   I will ever give to thee.

709 Hail to the Lord's anointed

Words: James Montgomery
based on Psalm 72

Music: from a melody in Johann Crüger's *Gesangbuch*
adapted by William Henry Monk

CRÜGER 76 76 D

1. Hail to the Lord's a-noint-ed, great Da-vid's great-er son! Hail, in the time ap-point-ed, his reign on earth be-gun! He comes to break op-pres-sion, to set the cap-tive free; to take a-way trans-gres-sion, and rule in e-qui-ty.

2. He comes with succour speedy
   to those who suffer wrong;
   to help the poor and needy,
   and bid the weak be strong;
   to give them songs for sighing,
   their darkness turn to light,
   whose souls, condemned and dying,
   were precious in his sight.

3. He shall come down like showers
   upon the fruitful earth,
   and love, joy, hope, like flowers,
   spring in his path to birth:
   before him on the mountains
   shall peace the herald go;
   and righteousness in fountains
   from hill to valley flow.

4. Kings shall fall down before him,
   and gold and incense bring;
   all nations shall adore him,
   his praise all people sing;
   to him shall prayer unceasing
   and daily vows ascend;
   his kingdom still increasing,
   a kingdom without end.

5. O'er ev'ry foe victorious,
   he on his throne shall rest,
   from age to age more glorious,
   all-blessing and all-blest;
   the tide of time shall never
   his covenant remove;
   his name shall stand for ever;
   that name to us is love.

710 Hallelujah, hosanna!

Words and Music: V. Masongo and M. DuPlessis
arr. Chris Mitchell

711 Have you been to Jesus

(Are you washed in the blood)

Words and Music: Elisha A. Hoffman

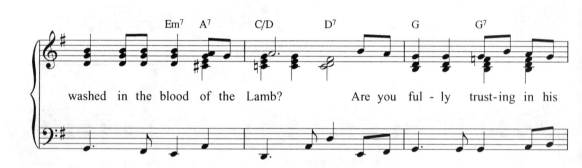

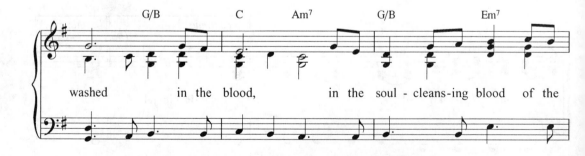

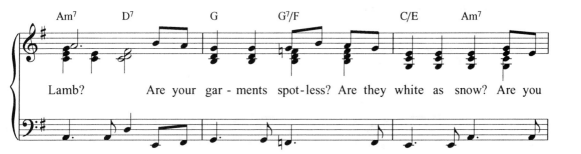

Lamb? Are your gar-ments spot-less? Are they white as snow? Are you

washed in the blood of the Lamb? 2. Are you Lamb?

To next verse | *Last time*

2. Are you walking daily by the Saviour's side?
   Are you washed in the blood of the Lamb?
   Do you rest each moment in the Crucified?
   Are you washed in the blood of the Lamb?

3. When the Bridegroom cometh will your robes be white?
   Are you washed in the blood of the Lamb?
   Will your soul be ready for the mansions bright,
   and be washed in the blood of the Lamb?

4. Lay aside the garments that are stained with sin,
   and be washed in the blood of the Lamb.
   There's a fountain flowing for the soul unclean,
   O be washed in the blood of the Lamb.

712 Have your way

Words and Music: Claire Cloninger and Don Moen
arr. Chris Mitchell

Have your way (have your way), have your way

(have your way), Ho - ly Spi - rit, fill our hearts

and have your way. As we wait

(we wait on you), as we pray (we pray to you),

*Optional counter-melody 2nd time

speak your word in - to our hearts

and have your way.

713 Hear our prayer

Words and Music: Tanya Riches
arr. Chris Mitchell

1. Hear our pray'r, Spi - rit, come.
2. On my knees I cry out,

How I long for your sweet touch.
Je - sus, Sa - viour, be - hold your child.

Like a deer long - ing for

wa - ter, my soul yearns. On - ly you can fill my deep

714 Hear our prayer

(Our Father)

Words and Music: Don Moen

1. Hear our pray'r, we are your child-ren, and we've

ga-thered here to-day; we've ga-thered here to pray;

hear our cry, we need your mer-cy, and

we need your grace to-day, hear us as we pray.

715 Hear these praises from a grateful heart
(Love you so much)

Words and Music: Russell Fragar

1. Hear these prai-ses from a grate-ful heart.
2. Lord I love you, my soul sings.

Each time I think of you the prai-ses start.
In your pre-sence car-ried on your wings. Love you so much,

Je - sus, love you so much.

so much.

so much. How my soul longs for

716 Heavenly Father

(Prayer song)

Words and Music: Ian Mizen and Andy Pressdee

Strongly rhythmic

1. Hea - ven-ly Fa - ther, may your ho-ly name be lift - ed

high in all the earth.

Hea-ven-ly Fa - ther, let your king-dom come, and your will be

done in all the earth.

2. Heavenly Father, wash away our sins
   and make us holy in your eyes.
   Heavenly Father, guide our hearts and minds
   and keep us hidden in your love.

Come, let us bow down in worship,
let us kneel before the Lord our Maker;
for he is our God
and we are the people of his pasture,
the flock under his care.

Psalm 95:6-7

717 He has come

(Prepare the way)

Words and Music: Darrell Evans and Eric Nuzum
arr. Chris Mitchell

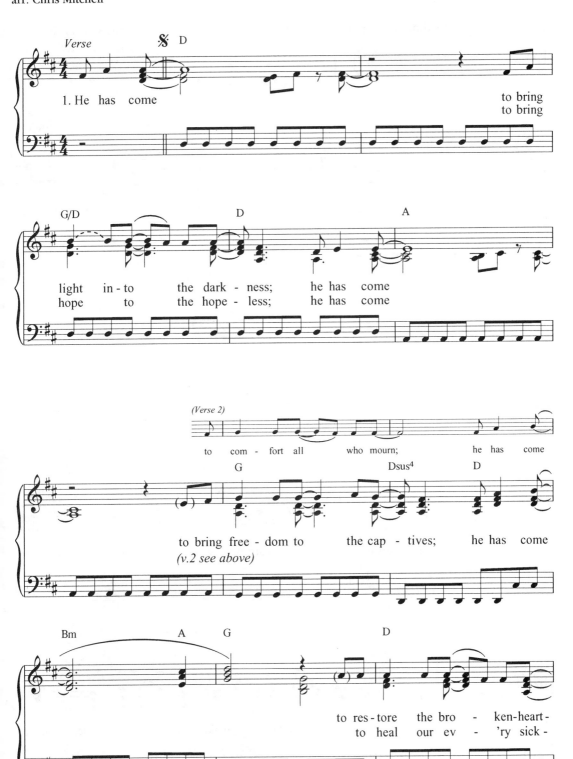

rea - dy the peo - ple of God, pre - pare the way.

2. He has come

718 He is able

Words and Music: Rory Noland and Greg Ferguson

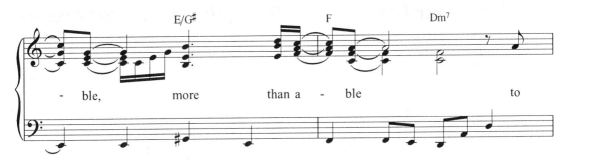

ble, more than a - ble to

do much more than I could e - ver dream. He is a -

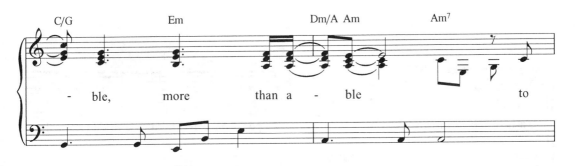

ble, more than a - ble to

make me what he wants me to be.

719 He is our God *(Everything that has breath)*

Words and Music: Michelle Hira
arr. Dave Bankhead

He is our God, let all cre - a - tion bow, the sov-'reign

King: most ho - ly One. He sac - ri - ficed his life,

washed and cleansed with - in, por - tioned by faith we're des - tined to

win. Ev - 'ry-thing that has breath, praise the Lord,

Therefore go and make disciples of all nations,
baptising them in the name of the Father
and of the Son and of the Holy Spirit,
and teaching them to obey
everything I have commanded you.
And surely I am with you always,
to the very end of the age.

Matthew 28:19-20

720 He is our peace

Words and Music: Kandela Groves
arr. Chris Mitchell

He is our peace, who has bro-ken down ev-'ry wall.

He is our peace, he is our peace. He is our

peace. Cast all your cares on him, for he cares for

you. He is our peace, he is our

peace. Cast all your peace.

721 Here I am *(I will always love your name)*

Words and Music: Paul Oakley

2. You took my sin, you took my shame,
   you drank my cup, you bore my pain:
   thank you, Lord;
   you broke the curse, you broke the chains,
   in victory from death you rose again:
   thank you, Lord;
   and not by works, but by your grace
   you clothe me now in your righteousness.

3. You bid me come, you make me whole,
   you give me peace, you restore my soul:
   thank you, Lord;
   you fill me up, and when I'm full
   you give me more till I overflow:
   thank you, Lord;
   you're making me to be like you,
   to do the works of the Father, too.

722 Here I am, in that old place again

(Sanctify)

Words: Stuart Garrard and Martin Smith

Music: Stuart Garrard

1. Here I am, in that old place a-gain, down on my face a-gain. Cry-ing out, I want you to hear my plea, come down and res-cue me. How long will it take? How long will I have to wait? And

2. Sanctify, I want to be set apart
   right to the very heart.
   Prophesy to the four winds
   and breathe life to this very place.
   How long will it take?
   How long will I have to wait?

3. Lifted up, I've climbed with the strength I have,
   right to this mountain top.
   Looking out, the cloud's getting bigger now,
   it's time to get ready now.
   How long will it take?
   How long will I have to wait?

723 Here I am once again   *(Pour out my heart)*

Words and Music: Craig Musseau

724 Here I am waiting

(Eagles' wings)

Words and Music: Reuben Morgan

Here I am wait - ing, a - bide in me I pray,

here I am long - ing for you.

Hide me in your love, bring me to my knees,

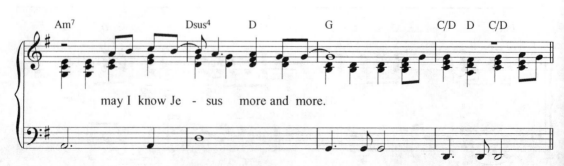

may I know Je - sus more and more.

725 Here, in the dawning *(Proclaim the favour of God)*

Words and Music: A. Smith, Johnny Markin and Chris Bowater

1. Here, in the dawn-ing of hope, in the wake of a ris-ing wave, clear, from the throne of our God comes a strength for ap-proach-ing days. We have a house God has called us to build, we have a chal-lenge be-fore us. Raise up your stan-dard in days such as these, for the year of his fa-vour has

2. Rise, for the light which has come
   is the glory that shines on you.
   See, though the darkness is strong,
   yet the nations will come to your light.
   We have a house God has called us to build,
   we have a challenge before us.
   Raise up your standard in days such as these,
   for the year of his favour has come.

Salvation is found in no one else,
for there is no other name under heaven given to men
by which we must be saved.

Acts 4:12

726 Here in this house   *(Awesome in this place)*

Words and Music: Ned Davies
arr. Chris Mitchell

Here in this house of the great King,
we've come to-ge-ther now to
wor-ship him. This house is built
on Christ our Rock, can-not be

shaken, cannot be shaken.

Chorus

God is awesome in this place,

we sense his presence as we

sing his praise. There is power here for

miracles, to set the captives free, and make the broken whole.

God is awesome, he's so awe-

727 Here in your presence

Words and Music: Colin Battersby

I was made to lift your

Chorus

name. 'Cause you're my God, on the throne, and my de-light

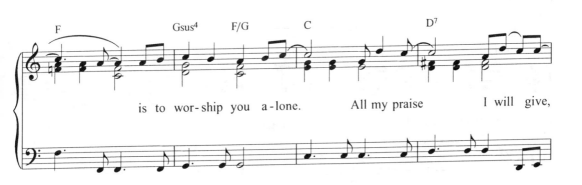

is to wor-ship you a-lone. All my praise I will give,

you are the rea - son why I live.

728 Here I stand before you   *(God of glory)*

Words and Music: Billie Mallett

1. Here I stand be-fore you, be-fore your throne of grace,

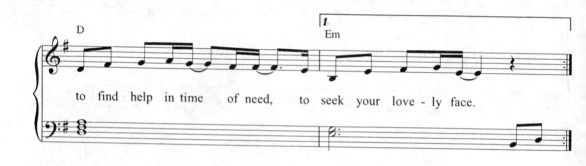

to find help in time of need, to seek your love-ly face.

seek your love-ly face. God of glo - ry, God of pow-

- er, God of ma - jes-ty. God of glo -

2. Fa - ther, I come to you

C
through the blood of Christ. D I bring to you an off-'ring of a

1. Em
con - se - cra - ted life.

2. Em
con - se - cra - ted life. D.S. God of glo -

729 Here is the risen Son

Words and Music: Michael Sandeman

Here is the ri-sen Son rid-ing out in glo-ry, ra-di-at-ing light all a-round. Here is the Ho-ly Spi-rit, poured out for the na-tions, glo-ri-fy-ing Je-sus the Lamb.

We will stand as a peo-ple who are up-right and ho-ly, we will wor-ship the Lord of hosts. We will

730 He rides on the wings of the wind

(Consuming fire)

Words and Music: Richard Lewis

He rides on the wings of the wind, his cha-ri-ot the clouds of hea-ven; ho-ly is he, ho-ly is he. He's clothed in a gar-ment of light, his mes-sen-gers are flames of fire; ho-ly is he, ho-ly is he. It's an awe-some thing,

2. His hair is as white as the snow, his eyes are a flame of fire;
   holy is he, holy is he.
   His feet are like glowing bronze, his voice like the many waters;
   holy is he, holy is he.

731 He shall be called 'Mighty!'

Words and Music: Mike Anderson
based on Isaiah 9, 11

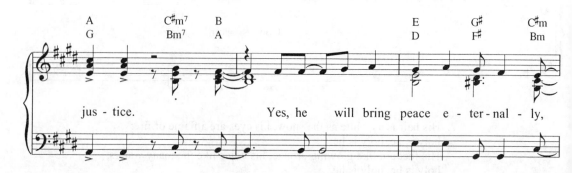

2. The goat shall lie down with the panther,
   the wolf with the lamb!
   The infant will play by the viper's lair,
   but never come to harm!

3. A child has been born to the people,
   a son given us!
   And he shall reign with integrity,
   and justice shall be ours!

732 He's the Saviour of my soul

Words and Music: Kathryn Kuhlman
arr. Richard Lewis

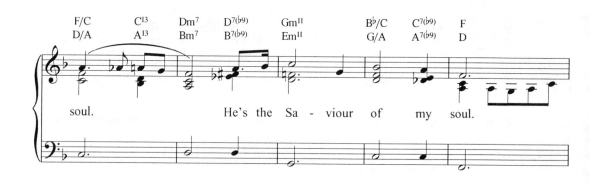

Je - sus, Je - sus. He's the Sa - viour of my

soul. He's the Sa - viour of my soul.

Hear my voice when I call to you.
May my prayer be set before you like incense.

Psalm 141:1b-2a

733 He who began a good work in you

Words and Music: Jon Mohr

A GOOD WORK Irregular

He who be-gan a good work in you, he who be-gan a good work in you will be faith-ful to com-plete it; he'll be faith-ful to com-plete it; he who start-ed the work will be faith-ful to com-plete it in you.

734 Hide me in the cleft of the rock

Words and Music: Dennis Jernigan
arr. Dave Bankhead

735 High above the dark horizon *(Morning star)*

Words: Graham Kendrick

Music: Graham Kendrick
arr. Jonathan Savage

High a-bove the dark hor-i-zon, we have seen the morn-ing star,

pro-mise of a cloud-less morn-ing lights up our hearts,

bright e-ter-nal day is break-ing, chas-ing sha-dows of the night,

o-pen fac-es up-ward gaz-ing, we a-wait the day of Christ.

2. Take the news to earth's far corners,
   soon the promised King will come,
   time's decay and death's dominion
   will soon be gone,
   there will be a new creation
   in the twinkling of an eye,
   hear his voice of invitation
   calling 'Don't be left behind.'

3. Coming soon on clouds descending
   east to west the skies will blaze,
   earth made bright with angel splendour,
   all the world amazed,
   ev'ry eye shall see his glory,
   King of kings and Lord of lords,
   saints from ev'ry age will greet him,
   caught up with him in the clouds.

4. So until that perfect morning
   we will run to win the race,
   till we're changed into his likeness,
   see him face to face,
   now unto the One who loves us,
   and redeemed us by his blood,
   be all honour, power and glory,
   so shall his kingdom come.

   Now unto the One who loves us,
   and redeemed us by his blood,
   be all honour, power and glory,
   so shall his kingdom come.
   Yes! Amen! Lord Jesus come!

736 High praises

Words and Music: Richard Lewis

Funky

Chorus

High prai-ses, high prai - ses, high prai-ses,

high prai - ses, high prai-ses, high prai - ses:

these are the prai - ses of hea - ven.

1. Leg - ions of an - gels in
2. Glo - ry and hon - our and

bright ar-ray wor ship the great 'I Am'. Sing-ing with joy of that
pow'r to him who's seat-ed up - on the throne. This is the e - ver-

glor-ious day when he will come to reign.
last - ing song that they sing to him a - lone.

Sing-ing

737 His name, his name

Words: unknown

Music: Jean Sibelius

FINLANDIA 10 10 10 10 10 10

His name, his name shall be called won-der-ful; his name, his name shall be called Coun-sel-lor. The Migh-ty God, the e-ver-last-ing Fa-ther, the Prince of Peace through all e-ter-ni-ty. The migh-ty God, the e-ver-last-ing Fa-ther, the Prince of Peace through all e-ter-ni-ty.

738 Holy breath of God

Words and Music: Johnny Markin

1. Ho - ly breath of God, find me in this place.

Fall, sweet mer - cy, fall on me, heal - ing by your grace.

Ten - der hand of God, hold me in your care.

All my fears and bro - ken dreams, ev - 'ry bur - den bear.

Come, O breath of God, breathe your life a -

2. Light of Life Divine, search my selfish ways.
   Tear from me my foolish will; lead me all my days.
   Ageless God of Hope, stay for ever near
   to the wounded broken heart; scatter ev'ry fear.

739 Holy fire

Words and Music: Steve Mitchinson and Brian Doerksen

Verse

1. Ho-ly fire from hea-ven, de-scend to us, we pray, let us burn a-gain.

Ho-ly fire from hea-ven, con-sume our hearts to-day, let us burn a-gain, let us burn a-gain.

Chorus

Wait-ing in ex-pec-tan-cy, sur-ren-dered to your sov-

-'reign - ty, we're hun - gry for true in - ti-ma - cy, Lord,

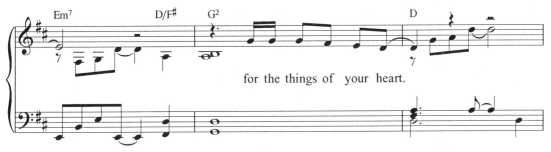

for the things of your heart.

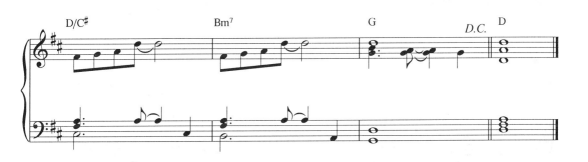

2. Holy breath from heaven, descend to us, we pray, let us breathe again.
   Holy breath from heaven, revive our hearts today, let us breathe again,
   let us breathe again.

3. Holy stream from heaven, descend to us, we pray, let us drink again.
   Holy stream from heaven, bring new life today, let us drink again,
   let us drink again.

740 Holy, holy, holy

Words and Music: Gary Oliver

Holy, holy, holy, holy, holy, holy, ly, holy is the Lord God Al-migh-ty! praise to-day.

Worthy to receive glory, worthy to receive honour, worthy to receive all our praise today.

Praise him, praise him and lift him up; praise him,

After this I looked
and there before me was a great multitude
that no one could count,
from every nation, tribe, people and language,
standing before the throne
and in front of the Lamb.
They were wearing white robes
and were holding palm branches in their hands.

Revelation 7:9

741 Holy, holy, holy is the Lord of hosts
(Holy is the Lord of hosts)

Words and Music: Nolene S. Prince
arr. Chris Mitchell

Ho-ly, ho-ly, ho-ly is the Lord of hosts. Ho-ly, ho-ly, ho-ly is the Lord of hosts. The whole earth is full of his glo - ry, the whole earth is full of his glo - ry, the whole earth is full of his glo - ry, ho-ly is the Lord.

742 Holy, holy, so holy

Words and Music: Richard Lewis

743 Holy is the Lord

Words and Music: Kelly Green
arr. Chris Mitchell

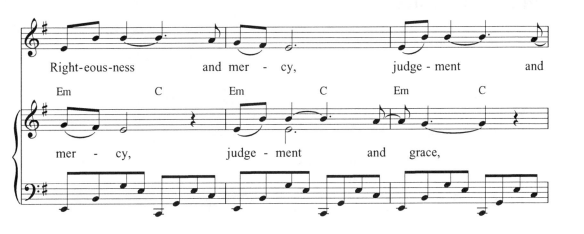

Right-eous-ness and mer - cy, judge - ment and

mer - cy, judge - ment and grace,

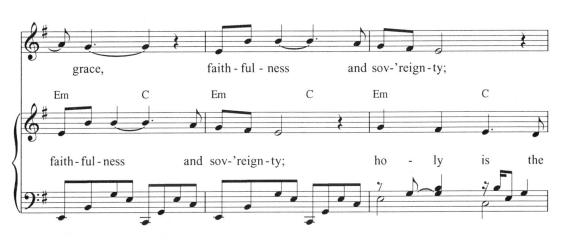

grace, faith - ful - ness and sov-'reign-ty;

faith - ful - ness and sov-'reign-ty; ho - ly is the

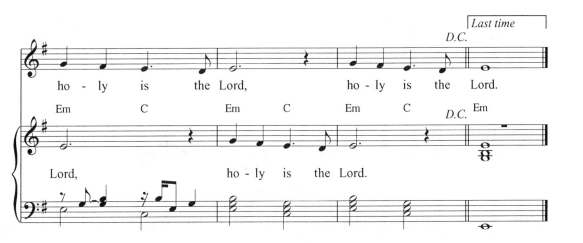

Last time
D.C.

ho - ly is the Lord, ho - ly is the Lord.

Lord, ho - ly is the Lord.

744 Holy Jesus

Words and Music: Ian Mizen and Andy Pressdee
arr. Chris Mitchell

Ho - ly Je - sus, burn your fire
Ho - ly Je - sus, full of grace

in me, ho - ly Je - sus,
and mer - cy, ho - ly Je - sus,

sanc - ti - fy. Son of God,
we lift you high.

Word of God, fill me up with your love.

Son of God,   Word of God,   fill me up with your

love, with your love,   with your love,

with your love,

with your love.

745 Holy Spirit, rain down

Words and Music: Russell Fragar

746 Holy Spirit, thou art welcome

Words and Music: Dottie Rambo and David Huntsinger
arr. Chris Mitchell

747 Hope has found its home within me

(For this cause)

Words and Music: Joel Houston
arr. Chris Mitchell

1. Hope has found its home with-in me
2. Let your pre-sence fall up-on us,

now that I've been found in you.
I want to see you face to face.

Let all I am be all you want me to be,
Let me live for e-ver lost in your love,

'cause all I want is more of you,

all I want is more of you.

2. 3.
F / D — C/E / A/C# — Dm⁷ / Bm⁷

All I want is you,

1.
B♭2 / G2

All I want is you,

Last time
B♭2 / G2 — F / D — *Fine*

All I want is you,

2.
B♭2 / G2 — F / D — C/E / A/C# — Dm⁷ / Bm⁷

All I want is, all I want is you, Je-sus.

B♭2 / G2 — F / D — C/E / A/C# — Dm⁷ / Bm⁷ — B♭2 / G2 — *D.S.*

All I want is, all I want is you, Je-sus.

748 How do I know you love me? *(I look to the cross)*

Words and Music: Mark Altrogge

1. How do I know you love me? I look a-round and see the sun-shine, the rain and the wind in the trees. But should these gra-cious to-kens all fade from my sight, I won't doubt your love for I fix my eyes. I look to the cross where I most clear-ly see your awe-some love dis-

2. How do I know you love me?
   At times I'm so aware.
   I sense your Holy Spirit,
   I see you ev'rywhere.
   But when I leave the mountain
   and your face is hid from sight,
   I won't doubt your love
   for I fix my eyes.

749 How great are you, Lord

Words and Music: Lynn De Shazo
arr. Chris Mitchell

How great are you, Lord, how great is your mer-

- cy. How great are the things that

you have done for me. How great are you, Lord,

your lov - ing kind - ness

750 How lovely is your dwelling-place

(Sing to my heart)

Words and Music: Joel Engle
arr. Chris Mitchell

Take hold of me and ne-ver let me go: I

long to hear you sing, sing to my heart.

751 How sweet your presence is

Words and Music: Wes Sutton

I want to rest in your love. If I should stray from your heart

run af - ter me, bring me home in your arms.

752 Humble yourselves

Words and Music: Dave Bilbrough

2. Open your hearts
   to the Lord your God,
   and know his love for you.

753 Hungry, I come to you *(Falling on my knees)*

Words and Music: Kathryn Scott
arr. Chris Mitchell

1. Hun-gry, I come to you, for I know you sat-is-fy.

I am emp-ty, but I know your love

does not run dry. So I wait for you;

so I wait for you. I'm fal-

- ling on my knees, of - fer - ing all of me.

Je - sus, you're all this heart is liv - ing for.

Last time

2. Broken, I run to you,
   for your arms are open wide.
   I am weary, but I know
   your touch restores my life.
   So I wait for you;
   so I wait for you.

754 I am yours
(Pure like you)

Words and Music: David Gate

2. I'm not afraid of earthly things,
   for I am safe with you, my King.

755 I believe in angels

Words and Music: Stuart Bell, Johnny Markin and Paul Cruikshank
arr. Dave Bankhead

1. I believe in angels, God's messengers of fire, and
2. I believe in worship that touches heaven's throne.
4. I believe revival will touch the earth again,

I believe in prophets who with God's word inspire, and
I believe his Spirit renews the faithful one.
I believe his Kingdom will rule without an end, and

I believe in miracles and that the strongholds fall, and
I believe the word of God, his truth revealed to all, yes,
I believe that unity will see his blessing fall, for

I believe in Jesus, the highest name of

756 I believe in the gospel   *(We believe)*

Words and Music: David Hind

you an - cient doors, that the King

Last chorus

may come in. O - pen your eyes,

bo - dy of Christ, see the King

now come in.

2. We believe there is mercy;
   we believe there is hope.
   We believe in forgiveness,
   that God's grace still shines forth.
   So we pray, Father, come now,
   release your fire, your Spirit in our land.
   We believe in Jesus Christ,
   the Son of God, he is alive.

3. We believe in the Church,
   it's the body of Christ on the earth.
   We believe there is one way,
   there's one faith, one baptism, one Lord.
   So we pray, Father, come now,
   release your fire, your Spirit in our land.
   We believe in Jesus Christ,
   the Son of God, he is alive.

Last Chorus:
So here he comes; this is his city
let the King now come in.
Open our eyes, he is alive;
see the King now come in.

The Spirit of the Sovereign Lord is on me,
because the Lord has anointed me
to preach good news to the poor.
He has sent me to bind up the broken-hearted,
to proclaim freedom for the captives
and release from darkness for the prisoners . . .

Isaiah 61:1

757 I bind unto myself today

Words: ascribed to St Patrick
trans. Cecil Frances Alexander

Music: traditional Irish melodies
arr. Charles Villiers Stanford

ST PATRICK'S BREASTPLATE Irregular

1. I bind unto myself today the strong name of the Trinity, by invocation of the same, the Three in One and One in Three.

PART II

DOXOLOGY

758 I call out to you, my Lord

(I surrender)

Words and Music: Wendy O'Connell
arr. Chris Mitchell

And I pray that you,
being rooted and established in love,
may have power, together with all the saints,
to grasp how wide and long and high and deep
is the love of Christ,
and to know this love that surpasses knowledge –
that you may be filled to the measure
of all the fullness of God.

Ephesians 3:17-19

759 I can feel the Spirit of God is moving
(Pour on your power)

Words and Music: Michael Battersby

I can feel the Spi-rit of God is mov - ing,

I can feel his pow-er in this place.

I be-lieve that God is more than a - ble

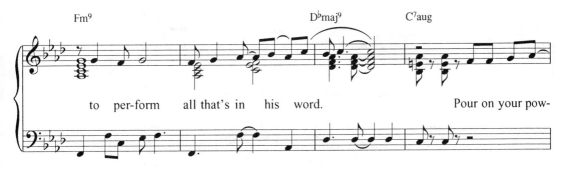

to per-form all that's in his word. Pour on your pow-

-er, Lord, dis - play your migh - ty strength.

This is the hour, Lord, when your peo-

- ple rise in faith. I take up the chal - lenge, Lord,

as I stand and take my place. Let the

760 I come to you

Words and Music: Andrew Bromley

I come to you, lay-ing my life be-fore you;

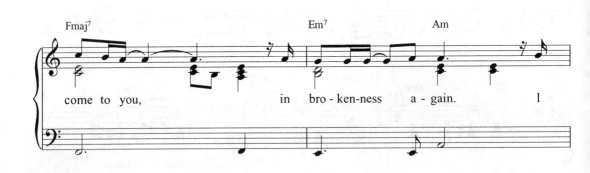

come to you, in bro-ken-ness a-gain. I

come to you, need-ing your grace and mer-cy,

come to you to know your love a-gain. Let your grace flow like a ri-

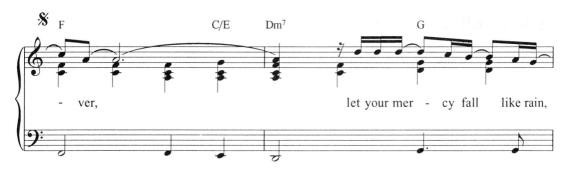

let your mer - cy fall like rain,

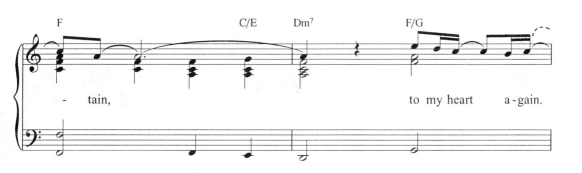

let your love be-come a foun -

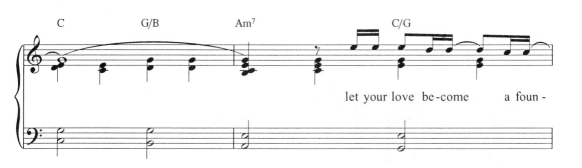

- tain, to my heart a-gain.

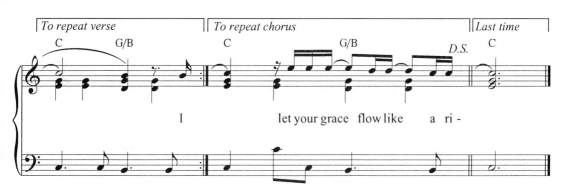

I let your grace flow like a ri -

761 I delight in you

Words and Music: Jeff Nelson

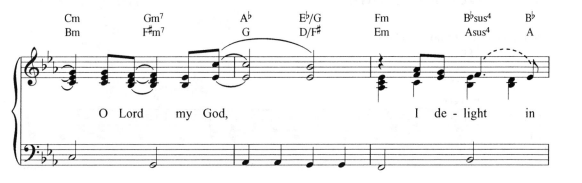

O Lord   my God,   I de - light   in

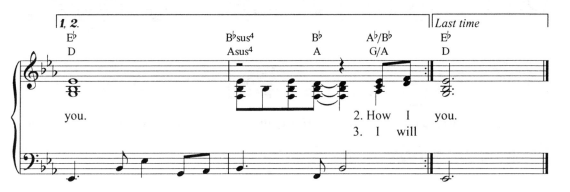

you.   2. How   I   you.
3.   I   will

2. How I love you, how I love you,
   O Lord my God.
   You're the only one I long for,
   how I love you, how I love you,
   O Lord my God,
   how I love you.

3. I will worship you, I will worship you,
   O Lord my God.
   You're the only one I long for,
   I will worship you, I will worship you,
   O Lord my God,
   I will worship you.

762 If we call to him
(Sing for joy)

Words and Music: Lamont Hiebert
arr. Chris Mitchell

1. If we call to him, he will ans-wer us; if we run to him, he will run to us; if we lift our hands, he will lift us up; come now, praise his name, all you saints of God.

O sing for joy to God, our strength; O

sing   for   joy   to   God,   our

strength,   our   strength.

2. Draw near to him, he is here with us;
    give him your love, he's in love with us;
    he will heal our hearts, he will cleanse our hands;
    if we rend our hearts, he will heal our land.

763 If you need Jesus, come

Words and Music: Scott Wesley Brown
arr. Richard Lewis

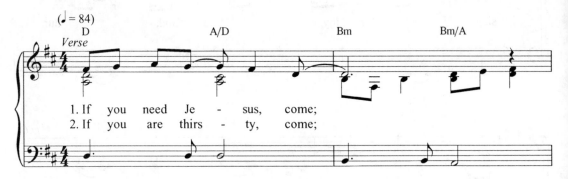

1. If you need Je - sus, come;
2. If you are thirs - ty, come;

if you need Je - sus, run;
if you are thirs - ty, run;
if you can see how great
if your heart cries and your soul

your need,
is dry,
fall on your knees and come.
fall on your knees and come.

If you need Je - sus, if you need Je - sus, come.

764 I have absolute trust

(Absolute trust)

Words and Music: J.B. Arthur
arr. Chris Mitchell

I have ab - so - lute trust in the In - fi - nite One who gave his life to me. In my ar - ro - gant, proud, self - ish state he reached down, he o - pened my eyes to see the vast ex - panse of his won - drous grace, for - give - ness and love.

765 I have been lifted up

Words and Music: David Wellington
arr. Richard Lewis

far a - way. There, there came a day,

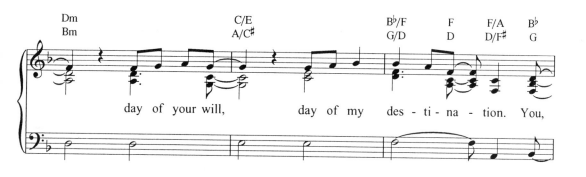

day of your will, day of my des - ti - na - tion. You,

you stole my heart mak-ing me so a-live.

D.C.

2. Now, now I have peace,
   peace in my heart,
   peace with Almighty living God,
   and you have sent,
   sent your own Spirit.
   We, we have been joined,
   joined two as one,
   joined as a holy temple;
   now no longer alone
   but part of your family.

766 I have decided to follow Jesus

Words: unknown

Music: Indian folk melody
arr. Chris Mitchell

Verse

C   C⁷/E

1. I have de - ci - ded to fol-low Je - sus, I have de-
hind me, the cross be - fore me; the world be-

F   F/C   C   C

ci - ded to fol-low Je - sus, I have de - ci - ded to fol-low
hind me, the cross be-fore me; the world be-hind me, the cross be-

Am⁷   Dm⁷   G⁷sus⁴   G⁷   C   C⁷/E

1.

Je - sus, no turn-ing back, no turn-ing back. 2. The world be-
fore me, no turn-ing back, no turn-ing

Last time   2.

C   C   C⁷/E   F   F/G

back.   back. No turn - ing back,

I have de - ci - ded to fol - low. No turn-ing back,

no turn-ing, no turn-ing, no turn-ing back. 3. Though none go

3. Though none go with me,
   I still will follow,
   though none go with me,
   I still will follow,
   though none go with me,
   I still will follow.
   No turning back,
   no turning back.

767 I have sung my songs of praise

(Make your home in me)

Words and Music: Michael Frye and Helen Frye
arr. Chris Mitchell

Now that I have felt your touch,

make your home in me.

2. I feel so safe with you,
acceptance in your voice;
you whisper tenderly:
'You are my belov'd, chosen one, my friend;
you're so precious to me.'

Great and marvellous are your deeds,
Lord God Almighty.
Just and true are your ways,
King of the ages.
Who will not fear you, O Lord,
and bring glory to your name?
For you alone are holy.
All nations will come
and worship before you,
for your righteous acts have been revealed.

Revelation 15:3-4

768 I know he rescued my soul   *(My Redeemer lives)*

Words and Music: Reuben Morgan

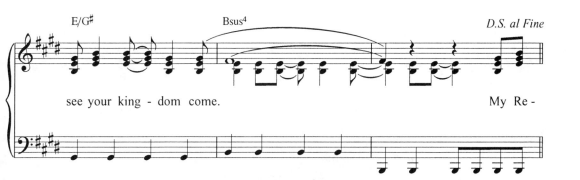

769 I know not why God's wondrous grace

Words: D.W. Whittle, alt. Stuart Townend

Music: Stuart Townend

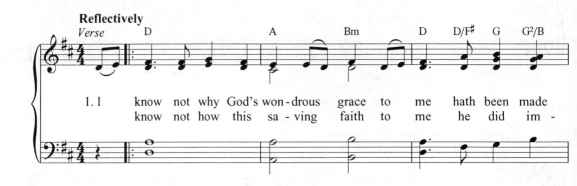

1. I know not why God's won-drous grace to me hath been made
   know not how this sa-ving faith to me he did im-

known; nor why, un-wor-thy as I am, he
part; or how be-liev-ing in his word wrought

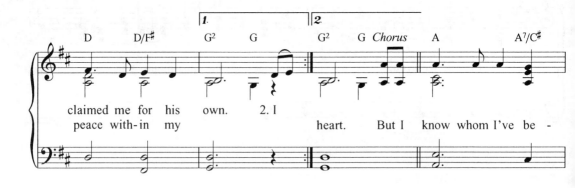

claimed me for his own. 2. I
peace with-in my heart. But I know whom I've be-

liev- ed; he's a-ble now to save what I've com-mit-ted

To continue   Last time

un - to him un - til that fi - nal day. day.

3. I know not how the Spirit moves,
   convincing men of sin;
   revealing Jesus through the word,
   creating faith in him.

4. I know not what of good or ill
   may be reserved for me,
   of weary ways or golden days
   before his face I see.

Chorus

5. I know not when my Lord may come;
   I know not how or where,
   if I shall pass the vale of death,
   or meet him in the air.

Chorus

770 I know you had me on your mind
(Redeemer, Saviour, Friend)

Words and Music: Darrell Evans
and Chris Springer, arr. Chris Mitchell

2. Ev'ry stripe upon your battered back,
   ev'ry thorn that pierced your brow,
   ev'ry nail drove deep through guiltless hands
   said that your love knows no end,
   Redeemer, Saviour, Friend.

3. So the grace you pour upon my life
   will return to you in praise,
   and I'll gladly lay down all my crowns
   for the name of which I'm saved,
   Redeemer, Saviour, Friend.

771 I lay my life down at your feet (All for you)

Words and Music: Andrew Bromley

I lay my life down at your feet, sur-ren-der all you've gi-ven me,

my fond-est thoughts, my wild-est dreams, all I am and hope to

be. I give my heart, I give my soul, to the one who gave his all,

to my Sa-viour, all to you.

772 I lift my eyes to you

(Intimate stranger)

Words and Music: Martin Smith
arr. Chris Mitchell

2. I lift my voice to you,
    lips that have cried a pray'r or two;
    beautiful stranger, fill my life.
    I lift my heart in praise to the Saviour
    whose death made all things new,
    intimate stranger, only you.

773 I lift up my eyes to your throne   *(River)*

Words and Music: Darlene Zschech and Reuben Morgan
arr. Dave Bankhead

I lift up my eyes to your throne, Lord, as I lose my-self in you.
The song in my heart will be yours a - lone.
My trea - sure is in the cross, Je-sus, I love to meet you there. I hun-ger and thirst for you, now flood my soul.

774 I'm giving you my heart

(Surrender)

Words and Music: Marc James
arr. Chris Mitchell

1. I'm giv-ing you my heart, and all that is with-in,
2. I'm sing-ing you this song; I'm wait-ing at the cross.

I lay it all down for the sake of you my
And all the world holds dear, I count it all as

King. I'm giv-ing you my dreams, I'm lay-ing down my rights,
loss. For the sake of know-ing you, the glo-ry of your name,

I'm giv-ing up my pride for the pro-mise of new
to know the last-ing joy, e-ven shar-ing in your

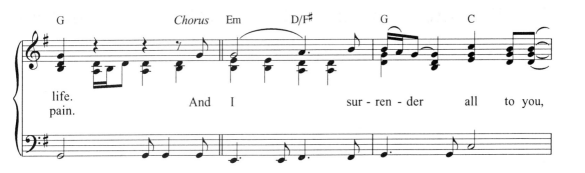

life.
pain.
And I sur - ren - der all to you,

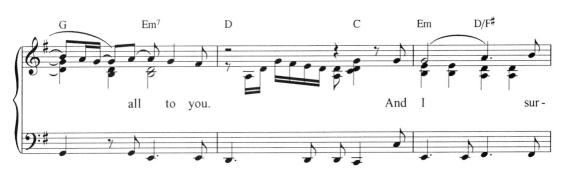

all to you. And I sur -

ren - der all to you, all to you.

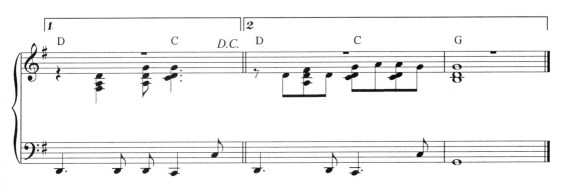

775 I'm gonna trust in God   *(Gonna trust in God)*

Words and Music: Steve Earl

1. I'm gon-na trust in God, I'm gon-na trust in Je - sus with-out shame and with-out fear, I'm gon-na fix my eyes on the hope of glo - ry for his day is draw-ing near.

Chorus

How great is the love of

2. Now when the cares of life seem overwhelming
   and my heart is sinking down,
   I'm gonna lift my hands to the one who'll help me,
   to the one who holds my crown.

776 I'm reaching for the prize

(Faith)

Words and Music: Reuben Morgan
arr. Chris Mitchell

Music: Reuben Morgan
arr. Chris Mitchell

777 I'm running the race

('Cause Jesus)

Words and Music: Kylie Adcock
arr. Chris Mitchell

run-ning the race, I'm mov-ing in faith, I'm walk-ing the walk, and I'm
put to the test, I'm giv-ing my best, I'm giv-ing my all, and I'm

talk-ing the talk; I'm shout-ing it out, and jump-ing a-bout, I'm
stand - ing tall; I'm a sol-dier of God, a child of the King, who

Worthy is the Lamb, who was slain,
to receive power and wealth and
wisdom and strength
and honour and glory and praise!

Revelation 5:12

778 I'm so glad, Jesus lifted me!

Words: unknown

Music: Camp Kirkland

Verses 1, 2, 5, 6, 7, 9 & 10

1. I'm so glad, Jesus lift-ed me! I'm so glad,
2. I'm so glad, Jesus set me free, I'm so glad,

Je-sus lift-ed me! I'm so glad, Je-sus lift-ed me! Sing-ing
Je-sus set me free! I'm so glad, Je-sus set me free, sing-ing

glo-ry, hal-le-lu-jah! Je-sus lift-ed me!
glo-ry, hal-le-lu-jah! Je-sus set me free.

Verses 3, 4 & 8

3. Sa-tan had me bound, but Je-sus set me free. Sa-tan had me bound, but
4. Out of sin and shame Je-sus set me free. Out of sin and shame

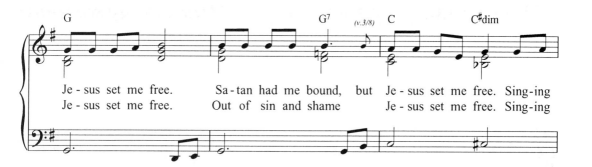

Je - sus set me free.   Sa - tan had me bound, but Je - sus set me free. Sing-ing
Je - sus set me free.   Out of sin and shame   Je - sus set me free. Sing-ing

glo - ry, hal - le - lu - jah!   Je - sus set me free.
glo - ry, hal - le - lu - jah!   Je - sus set me free.

5. I'm so glad Christ the Lord came down,
   I'm so glad Christ the Lord came down.
   Left his Father's glory, left his heav'nly crown.
   Oh, glory, hallelujah! I'm so glad.

6. I'm so glad he's my Lord and King,
   I'm so glad he's my Lord and King.
   That is why I praise him, that is why I sing.
   Oh, glory, hallelujah! I'm so glad.

7. I'm so glad he's living in my soul,
   I'm so glad he's living in my soul.
   Walking right beside me ev'rywhere I go.
   Oh, glory, hallelujah! I'm so glad.

8. On my way to heaven, I'll shout the victory.
   On my way to heaven, I'll shout the victory.
   On my way to heaven, I'll shout the victory.
   Singing glory, hallelujah, I shout the victory.

9. I'll tell the world Jesus lifted me.
   I'll tell the world Jesus lifted me.
   I'll tell the world Jesus lifted me;
   singing glory, hallelujah! Jesus lifted me.

10. I was bound, Jesus set me free.
    I was bound, Jesus set me free.
    I was bound, Jesus set me free;
    singing glory, hallelujah! Jesus lifted me.

779 I'm trading my sorrows *(Trading my sorrows)*

Words and Music: Darrell Evans

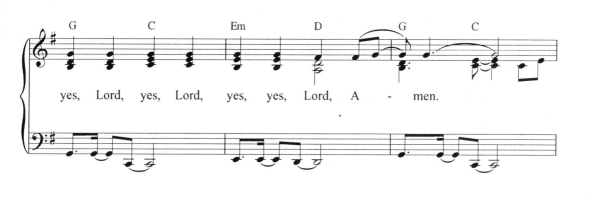

yes, Lord, yes, Lord, yes, yes, Lord, A - men.

I'm pressed but not crushed, per-se-cut-ed, not a-ban-doned,

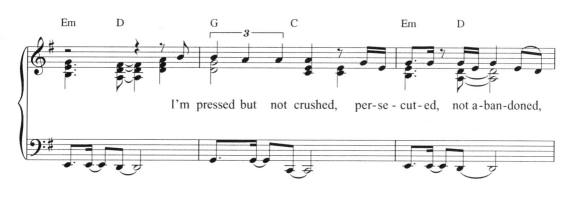

struck down, but not des-troyed; I'm blessed be-yond the curse, for his

pro-mise will en-dure, that his joy's gon-na be my strength.

Though the sor-row may last for a night, his joy comes with the morn-

CODA

D.C. al Coda

- ing.   La, la, la, la, la, la, la,

la, la, la, la, la, la, la, la, la, la, la, la, la, la, la, la,

la, la, la, la, la, la, la, la, la, la, A - men.

780 In awe of you we worship (*You are near*)

Words and Music: Reuben Morgan
arr. Chris Mitchell

In awe of you we wor - ship and stand a-mazed at your great love.

We're changed from glo- -ry to glo - ry; we set our hearts on you, our God.

781 I never want anything

(Heart and soul)

Words and Music: Wes Sutton

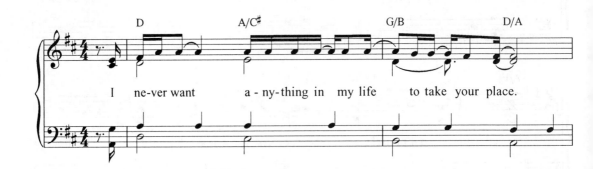

I ne-ver want a-ny-thing in my life to take your place.

I ne-ver want to live by a-ny o-ther grace. My

long-ing and my heart's de-sire is to see your face, O Lord,

and be-come a friend of God. I love you day and night,

I love you, all my life, I love you, Lord,

heart and soul, I long to be a friend of God.

782 In heavenly love abiding

Words: Anna Laetitia Waring
based on Psalm 23

Music: David Jenkins

PENLAN 76 76 D

1. In heav'n-ly love a-bid-ing, no change my heart shall

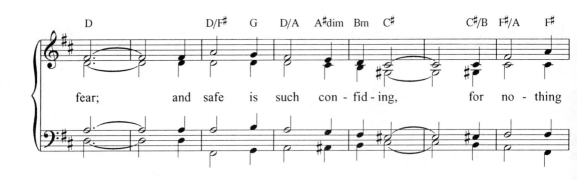

fear; and safe is such con-fid-ing, for no-thing

chang-es here. The storm may roar with-out me, my

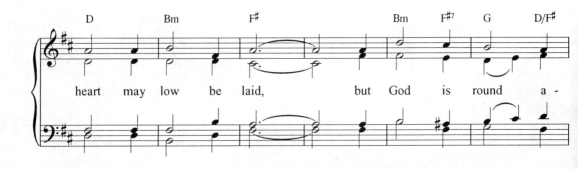

heart may low be laid, but God is round a-

bout me, and can I be dis - mayed?

2. Wherever he may guide me,
   no want shall turn me back;
   my Shepherd is beside me,
   and nothing shall I lack.
   His wisdom ever waketh,
   his sight is never dim,
   he knows the way he taketh,
   and I will walk with him.

3. Green pastures are before me,
   which yet I have not seen;
   bright skies will soon be o'er me,
   where the dark clouds have been.
   My hope I cannot measure,
   my path to life is free,
   my Saviour has my treasure,
   and he will walk with me.

Oh, the depth of the riches
of the wisdom and knowledge of God!
How unsearchable his judgements,
and his paths beyond tracing out!

For from him and through him
and to him are all things.
To him be the glory for ever! Amen.

Romans 11:33, 36

783 In his presence

Words and Music: Dick and Melodie Tunney

HIS PRESENCE Irregular

2. In your presence there is comfort,
   in your presence, there is peace.
   When we seek to know your heart
   we will find such bless'd assurance,
   in your holy presence, Lord.

784 In his presence there is joy   *(Holy ground)*

Words and Music: Geron Davis

In his pre-sence there is joy be-yond mea-sure, and at his feet peace of mind can still be found; and if you have a need, I know he has ev'ry ans-wer, but you've got to reach out and claim it, for you are

785 In my heart

Words and Music: Eric Grover

days I'll sing the prai - ses of his great re - deem - ing love.

2. In my heart there is a treason,
   one that poisons all my love.
   Take my heart and consecrate it,
   wash it in your cleansing flood.

3. Tie me to the Rock unchanging,
   tie me to his wondrous cross.
   I'll fix my eyes upon the Saviour,
   all other things I count as loss.

786 In my life

(Deeply in love)

Words and Music: Kate Spence
arr. Richard Lewis

CODA
F

Deep - ly in love.   deep - ly in love with you.

1.
C

2.
C   G

D.S.

In the year that King Uzziah died,
I saw the Lord seated on a throne,
high and exalted,
and the train of his robe filled the temple.
Above him were seraphs, each with six wings:
with two wings they covered their faces,
with two they covered their feet,
and with two they were flying.
And they were calling to one another:
'Holy, holy, holy is the Lord Almighty;
the whole earth is full of his glory.'

Isaiah 6:1-3

787 In my life proclaim your glory *(Lord of all mercy)*

Words and Music: Geoff Bullock

2. In my soul unveil your love, Lord,
   deep within my heart, renewing me.
   Day by day, your life transforming all I am,
   as this heart of mine reflects your praise.
   Lord of all, enthroned in glory,
   grace and mercy, truth and righteousness,
   ev'ry knee shall bow before this Christ, our Lord,
   as all creation sings your praise.

788 In so many ways you love me

(Adore)

Words and Music: Shonelle Barnes
arr. Chris Mitchell

In so ma-ny ways you love me just
pur-est love I've e-ver known was

as I am, not as I should be, and
that you chose to give and die, and the

as your child you take hold of me. I
blood that poured from your o-pen hands:

see just why I've fal-len in love with you.
all, so I could fall in love with you.

789 In the bleak midwinter

Words: Christina Georgina Rossetti

Music: Gustav Holst

CRANHAM Irregular

1. In the bleak mid-win – ter frost-y wind made moan, earth stood hard as ir – on, wa-ter like a stone; snow had fall-en, snow on snow, snow on snow, in the bleak mid-win-ter, long a – go.

2. Our God, heav'n cannot hold him
   nor earth sustain;
   heav'n and earth shall flee away
   when he comes to reign.
   In the bleak midwinter
   a stable-place sufficed
   the Lord God almighty,
   Jesus Christ.

3. Enough for him, whom cherubim
   worship night and day,
   a breastful of milk
   and a mangerful of hay:
   enough for him, whom angels
   fall down before,
   the ox and ass and camel
   which adore.

4. Angels and archangels
   may have gathered there,
   cherubim and seraphim
   thronged the air;
   but only his mother
   in her maiden bliss
   worshipped the belovèd
   with a kiss.

5. What can I give him,
   poor as I am?
   If I were a shepherd
   I would bring a lamb;
   if I were a wise man
   I would do my part,
   yet what I can I give him:
   give my heart.

Lord, I have heard of your fame;
I stand in awe of your deeds, O Lord.
Renew them in our day,
in our time make them known;
in wrath remember mercy.

Habakkuk 3:2

790 In the darkness
(Mercy-seat)

(Come running)

Words and Music: Steve Richardson, Mark Carouthers
and Jeff Harpole arr. Richard Lewis

1. In the dark - ness where ev - 'ry - thing is un-known
2. Are you liv - in' where hope has not been,

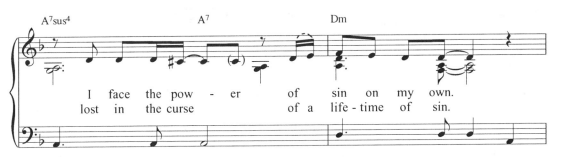

I face the pow - er of sin on my own.
lost in the curse of a life - time of sin.

I did not know of a place I could go
Love - ly il - lu - sions, they ne - ver come true,

where I could find a way to heal my wound-ed soul.
I know where there's a place of mer - cy for you.

seat where Je - sus is cal - lin', he said his grace would co - ver

me. His blood will flow free - ly, it will pro - vide the heal - ing.

I'm run - nin', I'm run - nin', I'm run - nin' to the mer - cy -

seat where Je - sus is cal - lin', he said his grace would co - ver

me. His blood will flow free - ly, it will pro - vide the heal - ing.

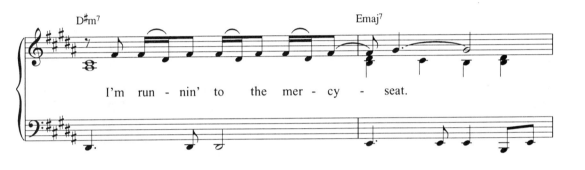

I'm run - nin' to the mer - cy - seat.

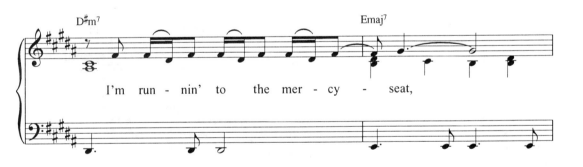

I'm run - nin' to the mer - cy - seat,

I'm run - nin' to the mer - cy - seat.

791 In the mornin' hour

Words and Music: Janine Price
arr. Chris Mitchell

Lyrics:

In the morn-in' hour, in the eve-nin' late, I'm gon-na praise your name. In the morn-in' hour, in the eve-nin' late, I'm gon-na praise your name. In the

For when I praise your name my strength is re-newed, you strength-en me, you strength-en me, you

792 Investigate

Words and Music: Martin Smith and Stuart Garrard
arr. Chris Mitchell

Praise the Lord.
How good it is to sing praises to our God,
how pleasant and fitting to praise him!

Psalm 147:1

793 In your presence there is joy

(God of glory)

Words and Music: Wayne and Libby Huirua

In your pres-ence there is joy, in your pres-ence there is free-dom, but the

great - est joy of all is to know we've made you smile. In your

pres - ence there is life, in your pres - ence there is heal - ing, but the

great - est joy of all is to know we've reached your heart.

794 I open my life to you *(Jesus, I adore you)*

Words and Music: Tanya Riches

I o-pen my life to you, Lord, I want to be pure.

Je - sus, you're breath to my soul; you

know what I think, what I feel. *Chorus* Je - sus, I a-

dore you; to you, my Sa-viour, I will sing, you

know me through and through; you're the clo-sest to my heart that one could be.

And, Je - sus, I a - dore you, I

love you with the deep - est of my soul, I

rest in-side your arms and I trust you to lead me on.

795 I see the Lord

Words and Music: Paul Baloche

796 I see you now *(High above the nations)*

Words and Music: Matthew Lockwood

1. I see you now, I see you high and lift-ed up, I see your glo-ry fill the whole earth, I see your throne, I see your ma-jes-ty and splen-dour, and I join with an-gels cheer-ing:

Chorus

Glo - ry, glo - ry, glo-ry to the Lamb en-throned on high. Glo - ry, glo - ry to the Lamb up-on the

797 Isn't it good

Words and Music: Janine Price
arr. Chris Mitchell

798 It came upon the midnight clear

Words: Edmund Hamilton Sears, alt.

Music: traditional English melody
arr. Arthur Seymour Sullivan

NOEL DCM

2. Still through the cloven skies they come,
   with peaceful wings unfurled;
   and still their heav'nly music floats
   o'er all the weary world:
   above its sad and lowly plains
   they bend on hov'ring wing;
   and ever o'er its Babel-sounds
   the blessèd angels sing.

3. Yet with the woes of sin and strife
   the world has suffered long;
   beneath the angel-strain have rolled
   two thousand years of wrong;
   and warring humankind hears not
   the love-song which they bring:
   O hush the noise of mortal strife,
   and hear the angels sing!

4. And ye, beneath life's crushing load,
   whose forms are bending low,
   who toil along the climbing way
   with painful steps and slow:
   look now! for glad and golden hours
   come swiftly on the wing;
   O rest beside the weary road,
   and hear the angels sing.

5. For lo, the days are hast'ning on,
   by prophets seen of old,
   when with the ever-circling years
   comes round the age of gold;
   when peace shall over all the earth
   its ancient splendours fling,
   and all the world give back the song
   which now the angels sing.

Praise be to the God and Father
of our Lord Jesus Christ!
In his great mercy
he has given us new birth into a living hope
through the resurrection of Jesus Christ from the dead.

1 Peter 1:3

799 I thank the Lord *(Everybody praise the Lord)*

Words and Music: Lincoln Brewster
arr. Chris Mitchell

Not to us, O Lord, not to us
but to your name be the glory,
because of your love and faithfulness.

Psalm 115:1

800 I thank you for the precious blood
(Thank you for the blood)

Words: Colin Dye and Richard Lewis
(revised and adapted by Richard Lewis)

Music: Richard Lewis

'Thank you for the blood, thank you for the blood; the

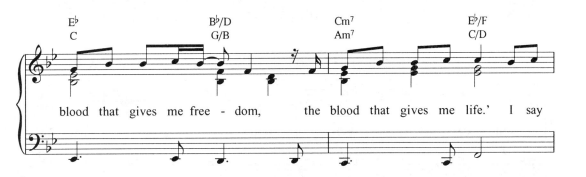

blood that gives me free - dom, the blood that gives me life.' I say

'Thank you for the blood, thank you for the blood,

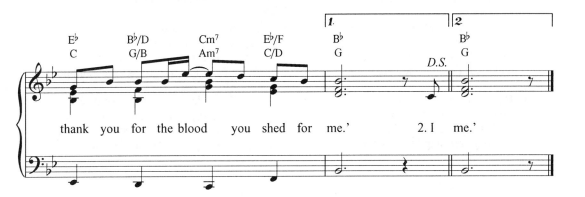

thank you for the blood you shed for me.' 2. I me.'

801 It is a thing most wonderful

Words: William Walsham How

Music: Thomas Bishop Southgate

BROOKFIELD LM

1. It is a thing most won - der - ful, al - most too won - der - ful to be, that God's own Son should come from heav'n, and die to save a child like me.

2. And yet I know that it is true:
   he chose a poor and humble lot,
   and wept and toiled, and mourned and died,
   for love of those who loved him not.

3. I sometimes think about the cross,
   and shut my eyes, and try to see
   the cruel nails and crown of thorns,
   and Jesus crucified for me.

4. But even could I see him die,
   I could but see a little part
   of that great love which, like a fire,
   is always burning in his heart.

5. I cannot tell how he could love
   a child so weak and full of sin;
   his love must be most wonderful,
   if he could die my love to win.

6. It is most wonderful to know
   his love for me so free and sure;
   but 'tis more wonderful to see
   my love for him so faint and poor.

7. And yet I want to love thee, Lord;
   O light the flame within my heart,
   and I will love thee more and more,
   until I see thee as thou art.

802 It is good

Words and Music: Dan Adler

With a Latin feel

It is good, it is good, it is good to give thanks to the
play on our in-stru-ments sweet songs of praise for the

Lord on high,   to sing of your faith-ful-ness
things you do.   It is good, it is good, it is

1. and lov-ing kind-ness both day and night;   to

2. *After 2nd verse to Bridge*   *Fine*
good to give thanks to you.

803 It passeth knowledge

Words: Mary Shekleton

Music: Ira David Sankey

IT PASSETH KNOWLEDGE 10 10 10 10 4

1. It passeth knowledge, that dear love of thine, my Saviour, Jesus! yet this soul of mine would of thy love, in all its breadth and length, its height and depth, and e-ver-last-ing strength, know more and more.

2. It passeth telling, that dear love of thine,
my Saviour, Jesus! yet these lips of mine
would fain proclaim, to sinners, far and near,
a love which can remove all guilty fear,
and love beget.

3. It passeth praises, that dear love of thine,
my Saviour, Jesus! yet this heart of mine
would sing that love, so full, so rich, so free,
which brings a rebel sinner, such as me,
nigh unto God.

4. O fill me, Saviour Jesus, with thy love;
lead, lead me to the living fount above;
thither may I, in simple faith, draw nigh,
and never to another fountain fly,
be unto thee.

5. And then, when Jesus face to face I see,
when at his lofty throne I bow the knee,
then of his love, in all its breadth and length,
its height and depth, its everlasting strength,
my soul shall sing.

804 I trust in you, my faithful Lord
(I will bless you, Lord)

Word and Music: Darlene Zschech

805 It's all for you

Words and Music: Mark Altrogge

1. It's all for you, cre-a-tion, Lord, the u-
   for you, the one who came to seek

-ni-verse, it's all for you.
and serve, it's all for you,

The star-
who died

-ry sky, the em-'rald earth, it's all for you,
the death that we de-serve, it's all for you,

all to bring you glo—ry. It's all

all to bring you glo—ry. It's all for

2. It's all for you, our joy, our adoration,
   Lord, it's all for you.
   Our songs, our celebration, Lord, it's all for you,
   all to bring you glory, it's all for you.
   Our trials and temptations, Lord, they're all for you.
   Our suffering, our patience,
   Lord, it's all for you, all to bring you glory.

806 I've come to this house to celebrate

(God is so good)

Words and Music: Michael Battersby

I've come to this house to ce-le-brate the good-ness of God in my life, and for all that you've done. And af-ter ev-'ry-thing you give to me the best is still to come. So I de-di-cate my life to seek-ing your face, 'cause

In that day you will say:
'Give thanks to the Lord, call on his name;
make known among the nations what he has done,
and proclaim that his name is exalted.
Sing to the Lord, for he has done glorious things;
let this be known to all the world.'

Isaiah 12:4-5

807 I wait in your sanctuary

Words and Music: Wes Sutton

I wait in your sanc-tu - a - ry to be-hold your glo - ry, the glo - ry of my God and King. I bow down be-fore you to wor-ship and a - dore you, my God, the Ho -ly One, the King.

'Where, O death, is your victory?
Where, O death, is your sting?'
The sting of death is sin,
and the power of sin is the law.
But thanks be to God!
He gives us the victory through our Lord Jesus Christ.

1 Corinthians 15:55-57

808 I want to be holy

Words and Music: Paul Oakley and Alan Rose

I want to be ho-ly, I want to be right-eous, I want to live my life the way you want me to. I want to be blame-less, not walk-ing in dark-ness, I want to be a liv-ing sac-ri-fice to you. I'm gon-na run the race, I'm gon-na run to win,

809 I want to seek your face
(Better than life)

Words and Music: Joel Engle
arr. Chris Mitchell

I want to seek your face, I want to know your ways,

I want to give you praise, O Lord, most high.

You are the ho-ly One, you are the a-noint-ed One,

you are the on-ly One. And your

The heavens declare the glory of God;
the skies proclaim the work of his hands.

Psalms 19:1

810 I was on your mind

(On your mind)

Words and Music: Mick Dalton
arr. Dave Bankhead

811 I will awaken the dawn

Words and Music: Richard Lewis

Shout for joy to the Lord, all the earth.
Worship the Lord with gladness;
come before him with joyful songs.
Know that the Lord is God.
It is he who made us, and we are his;
we are his people, the sheep of his pasture.

Enter his gates with thanksgiving
and his courts with praise;
give thanks to him and praise his name.
For the Lord is good and his love endures for ever;
his faithfulness continues through all generations.

Psalm 100

812 I will bless the Lord at all times *(Everything)*

Words and Music: Mark Naea and Vernon Katipa

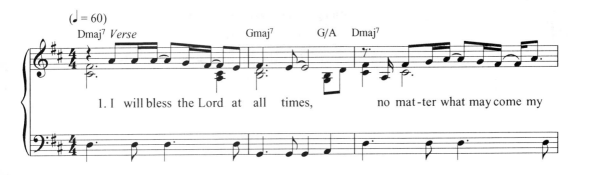

1. I will bless the Lord at all times, no mat-ter what may come my

way; al-ways look-ing un-to Je - sus,

the au-thor of my faith. As my heart is filled with

prai-ses I will glo-ri-fy your name.

Lord, I give you ev - 'ry-thing and wor - ship you, my one and on - ly

King; you are wor-thy of all prai - ses. Lord, I give my heart and soul, in

ev - 'ry-thing I do in you I know you will be glo - ri-fied.

Fine

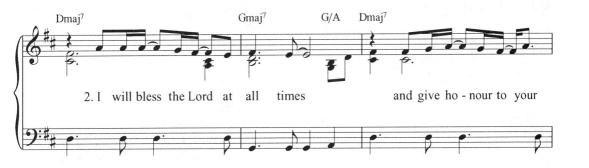

2. I will bless the Lord at all times and give ho-nour to your

name. All I have I will sur-ren - der;

Ho-ly Spi-rit have your way. Take this ves-sel, Lord, and

D.S. al Fine

use me to bring glo-ry to your name.

813 I will celebrate

Words and Music: Rita Baloche

I will ce-le-brate, sing un-to the Lord,

sing to the Lord a new song.

I will ce-le-brate, sing un-to the Lord,

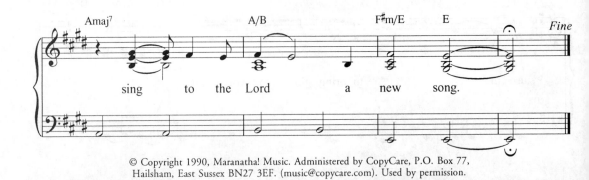

sing to the Lord a new song.

With my heart re - joic - ing with - in, with my

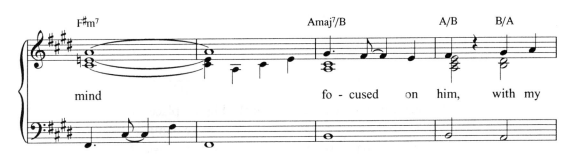

mind fo - cused on him, with my

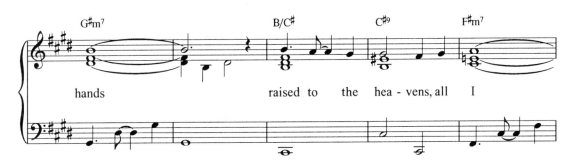

hands raised to the hea - vens, all I

D.C. al Fine

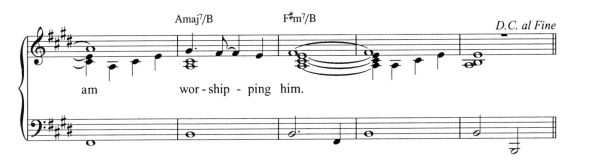

am wor - ship - ping him.

Therefore God exalted him to the highest place
and gave him the name that is above every name,
that at the name of Jesus every knee should bow,
in heaven and on earth and under the earth,
and every tongue confess that Jesus Christ is Lord,
to the glory of God the Father.

Philippians 2:9-11

814 I will come and bow down

Words and Music: Martin Nystrom
arr. Chris Mitchell

I will come and bow down at your feet, Lord Je - sus. In your pre - sence is full - ness of joy. There is no - thing, there is no one who com - pares with you. I take plea - sure in wor - ship - ping you, Lord.

815 I will come into your presence   *(Lift him up)*

Words and Music: Billy Funk
arr. Chris Mitchell

I will come in - to your pre - sence, Lord,
I will give you all the glo - ry,

with a sac - ri - fice of praise;
you de - li - vered me from shame;

with a song I will ex - alt you, Lord,
I'm cre - a - ted in your right - eous-ness,

bles - sed be your ho - ly name.
bles - sed be your ho - ly name.

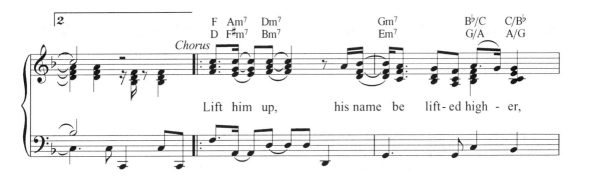

Chorus

F Am⁷ Dm⁷   Gm⁷   B♭/C   C/B♭
D F♯m⁷ Bm⁷   Em⁷   G/A   A/G

Lift him up,   his name be   lift-ed high - er,

Am⁷   Dm⁷   Gm⁷   B♭/C   C⁷
F♯m⁷   Bm⁷   Em⁷   G/A   A⁷

lift him up,   ex-alt his ho-ly name;

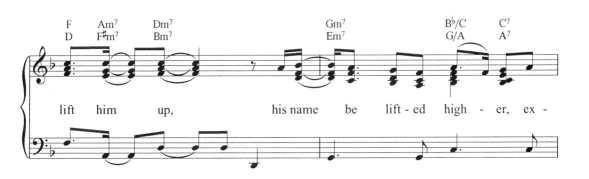

F Am⁷ Dm⁷   Gm⁷   B♭/C   C⁷
D F♯m⁷ Bm⁷   Em⁷   G/A   A⁷

lift him up,   his name be   lift-ed high - er, ex -

1.
Gm⁷   B♭/C   C⁷   F
Em⁷   G/A   A⁷   D

Fm⁷/A♭ Gm⁷ B♭/C
Dm⁷/F Em⁷ G/A

2.

alt his ho - ly name.

816 I will come to you (*Lord, your goodness*)

Words and Music: Reuben Morgan

I will come to you with an o-pen heart,

bring a sac-ri-fice of praise. I have

seen your pow'r in the ho-ly place,

I have known your migh-ty ways. I will re-mem-

-ber your mer-cy, and,

817 I will give thanks to thee

(Be exalted)

Words and Music: Brent Chambers
arr. Roland Fudge

Rich and unhurried

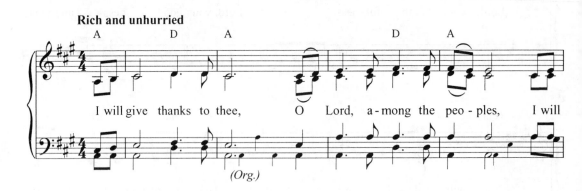

I will give thanks to thee, O Lord, a-mong the peo - ples, I will

(Org.)

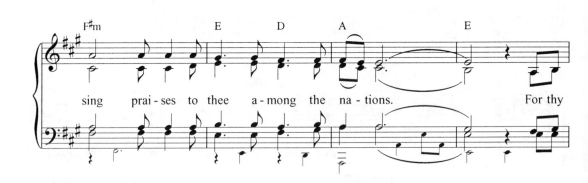

sing prai - ses to thee a - mong the na - tions. For thy

stead - fast love is great, is great to the hea - vens, and thy

faith-ful-ness, thy faith-ful-ness, to the clouds. Be ex -

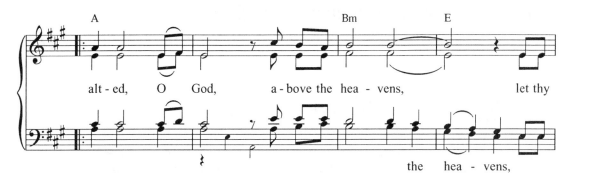

alt - ed, O God, a - bove the hea - vens, let thy the hea - vens,

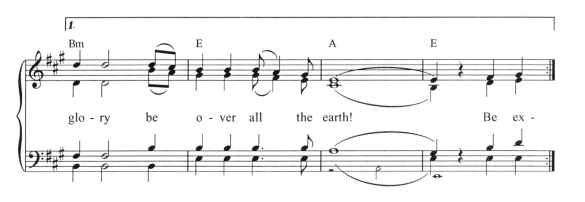

1.

glo - ry be o - ver all the earth! Be ex -

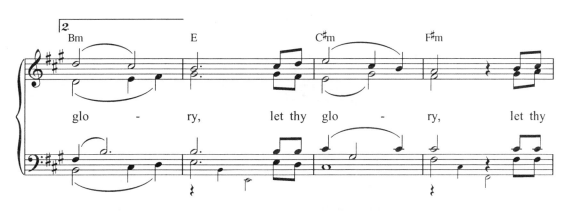

2

glo - ry, let thy glo - ry, let thy

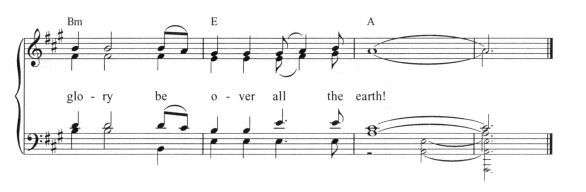

glo - ry be o - ver all the earth!

818 I will live to declare your glory
(You are the Holy One)

Words and Music: Joel Engle
arr. Chris Mitchell

For where two or three come together in my name, there am I with them.

Matthew 18:20

819 I will not live by power *(Power or might)*

Words and Music: Wes Sutton

820 I will sing of your faithfulness *(This is the day)*

Words and Music: Matt Poole

joy of the Lord shall be our strength. I was born to be your

dwel - ling - place. This is the day that the Lord has made.

821 I will sing the wondrous story

Words: Francis Harold Rowley

Music: Rowland Hugh Prichard
arr. Ralph Vaughan Williams

HYFRYDOL 87 87 D

I will sing the won - drous sto - ry of the

Christ who died for me; how he left his

home in glo - ry, for the cross on Cal - va -

ry. I was lost: but Je - sus found me — found his

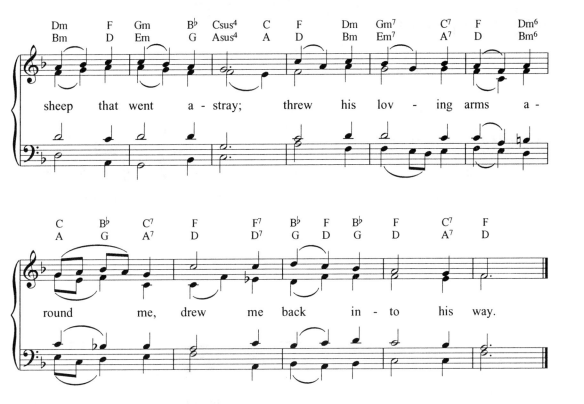

sheep that went a-stray; threw his lov-ing arms a-round me, drew me back in-to his way.

2. I was bruised; but Jesus healed me —
faint was I from many a fall;
sight was gone, and fears possessed me:
but he freed me from them all.
Days of darkness still come o'er me;
sorrow's paths I often tread:
but the Saviour still is with me,
by his hand I'm safely led.

3. He will keep me till the river
rolls its waters at my feet;
then he'll bear me safely over,
where the loved ones I shall meet.
Yes, I'll sing the wondrous story
of the Christ who died for me;
sing it with the saints in glory,
gathered by the crystal sea.

822 I will testify

Words and Music: Richard Lewis

I will tes - ti - fy of the Sa - viour whom I love, who laid down his life for all my guilt and shame. He was cru - ci - fied to take a - way my sin;

he has paid the price with his ne - ver end - ing love.

Deep as the o - cean, high as the

high - est heav'n a - bove, wide as the east is from the west

1. is your great love.

2. is your great love.

823 I will wait

(More)

Words and Music: Reuben Morgan
arr. Chris Mitchell

all my heart. I want to know

you, you are all I want.

I want to know you more.

824 I will worship

Words and Music: Geoff Bullock
arr. Dave Bankhead

825 Jesus, all for Jesus

Words and Music: Jennifer Atkinson and Robin Mark

1. Je - sus, all for Je - sus; all I am and have and e - ver hope to be.

be. be.

826 Jesus, be the centre

(Be the centre)

Words and Music: Michael Frye
arr. Chris Mitchell

be the rea - son that I live, Je - sus,

Je - sus.

3. Jesus, be my vision,
    be my path, be my guide,
    Jesus.

The Lord is my rock, my fortress and my deliverer;
my God is my rock, in whom I take refuge.
He is my shield and the horn of my salvation, my stronghold.

The Lord lives! Praise be to my Rock!
Exalted be God my Saviour!

Psalm 18:2, 46

827 Jesus Christ, you are the Son of God

(On my knees)

Words and Music: Andy Pressdee and Ian Mizen
arr. Richard Lewis

1. Je-sus Christ, you are the Son of God, Ho-ly One, you gave ev-'ry-thing to be-come like one of us. Hea-ven's Son came to earth,

2. You o-beyed God's plan to the ve-ry end, Ho-ly One, be-came the sac-ri-fice that would show us the Fa-ther's love. You came to die to give us life,

One day all the world will see you, one day all the world will see all cre - a - tion kneel be - fore you, all cre - a - tion sing.

Last time

828 Jesus, how I love your name

Words and Music: Mike Norman & Mike Little
arr. Dave Bankhead

Je - sus, how I love your name, I will sing your praise for e-ver and

e - ver. Je - sus, how you've set me free, I will

mag - ni-fy your name in hon-our and glo - ry to-day.

1st time

Last time   *Fine*

Lord, with-out you I am

829 Jesus, how we love you *(The glory of the ages)*

Words and Music: Steve and Vikki Cook

830 Jesus, I see in you

Words and Music: Wes Sutton

Lift up your heads, O you gates;
be lifted up, you ancient doors,
that the King of glory may come in.
Who is this King of glory?
The Lord strong and mighty,
the Lord mighty in battle.
Lift up your heads, O you gates;
lift them up, you ancient doors,
that the King of glory may come in.
Who is he, this King of glory?
The Lord Almighty –
he is the King of glory.

Psalm 24:7-10

831 Jesus, Jesus

(Jesus, open the heavens)

Words and Music: Jayne and Luke Weller
arr. Richard Lewis

832 Jesus, Jesus

(Take me as I am)

Words and Music: Suzette Thorndycraft

Take me as I am and I will call you Lord,

come, take me here and now, and be my Sa-

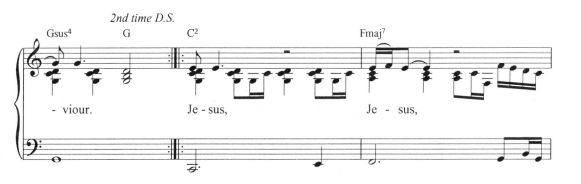

2nd time D.S.

- viour. Je - sus, Je - sus,

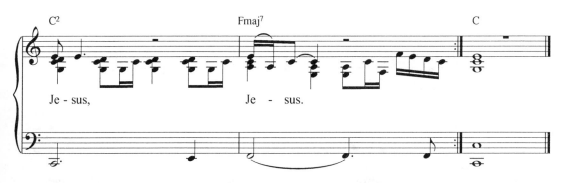

Je - sus, Je - sus.

833 Jesus, Jesus, Jesus
(There's something about that name)

Words and Music: William J. Gaither and Gloria Gaither
arr. Richard Lewis

Je - sus, Je - sus, Je - sus; there's just

some-thing a - bout that name. Mas - ter,

Sa - viour, Je - sus, like the fra - grance af - ter the

rain. Je - sus, Je - sus, Je -

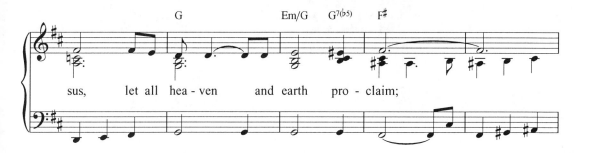

sus,   let all hea - ven   and earth pro - claim;

kings   and   king - doms   will   all   pass a - way,   but there's

some - thing   a - bout   that   name.

This righteousness from God
comes through faith in Jesus Christ
to all who believe.
There is no difference,
for all have sinned
and fall short of the glory of God,
and are justified freely by his grace
through the redemption that came by Christ Jesus.

Romans 3:22-24

834 Jesus, keep me near the Cross   *(Near the Cross)*

Words: Frances Jane van Alstyne
(Fanny J. Crosby)

Music: William Howard Doane

2. Near the Cross, a trembling soul,
   love and mercy found me;
   there the bright and morning star
   shed its beams around me.

3. Near the Cross: O Lamb of God,
   bring its scenes before me;
   help me walk from day to day,
   with its shadow o'er me.

4. Near the Cross I'll watch and wait,
   hoping, trusting ever,
   till I reach the golden strand,
   just beyond the river.

835 Jesus, King of kings

Words and Music: Chris Rolinson

Worshipfully (slow 4)

1. Je - sus, King of kings, we wor - ship and a -

dore you. Je - sus, Lord of heav'n and earth, we

bow down at your feet. Fa - ther, we

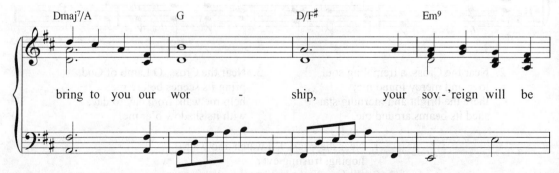

bring to you our wor - ship, your sov - 'reign will be

done, on earth your king - dom come, through

Je - sus Christ, your on - ly Son.

2. Jesus, sov'reign Lord,
   we worship and adore you.
   Jesus, name above all names,
   we bow down at your feet.
   Father, we offer you our worship,
   your sov'reign will be done,
   on earth your kingdom come,
   through Jesus Christ, your only Son.

3. Jesus, light of the world,
   we worship and adore you.
   Jesus, Lord Emmanuel,
   we bow down at your feet.
   Father, for your delight we worship,
   your sov'reign will be done,
   on earth your kingdom come,
   through Jesus Christ, your only Son.

836 Jesus, Light of the world

Words and Music: Geoff Baker

Je - sus, Light of the world, shine your

light on me. Je - sus,

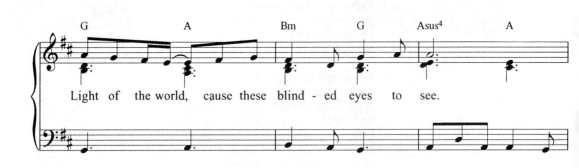

Light of the world, cause these blind - ed eyes to see.

See your glo - ry, see your face, know the joy of your

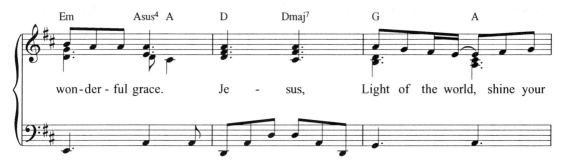

Em   Asus⁴ A   D   Dmaj⁷   G   A

won - der - ful grace.   Je - sus,   Light of the world, shine your

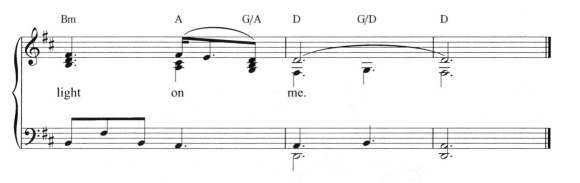

Bm   A   G/A   D   G/D   D

light   on   me.

2. Jesus, Hope of the world,
   set your hope in me.
   Jesus, Hope of the world,
   cause these blinded eyes to see.
   See your sov'reign will be done,
   know by faith that your Kingdom is come.
   Jesus, Hope of the world,
   set your hope in me.

3. Jesus, Joy of the world
   put your joy in me.
   Jesus, Joy of the world,
   cause these blinded eyes to see.
   See the vict'ry of the cross,
   know the place you're preparing for us.
   Jesus, Joy of the world
   put your joy in me.

837 Jesus, lover of my soul

(It's all about you)

Words and Music: Paul Oakley

all my days. For no-one else in his-to-ry is

like you, and his-to-ry it-self be-longs to you.

838 Jesus, lover of my soul

Words: Charles Wesley

Music: Joseph Parry

ABERYSTWYTH 77 77 D

1. Je - sus, lov - er of my soul, let me to thy bo - som fly,

while the near - er wa - ters roll, while the tem - pest still is high;

hide me, O my Sa - viour, hide, till the storm of life is past;

safe in - to the ha - ven guide, O re - ceive my soul at last.

2. Other refuge have I none,
   hangs my helpless soul on thee;
   leave, ah, leave me not alone,
   still support and comfort me.
   All my trust on thee is stayed,
   all my help from thee I bring;
   cover my defenceless head
   with the shadow of thy wing.

3. Thou, O Christ, art all I want;
   more than all in thee I find;
   raise the fallen, cheer the faint,
   heal the sick, and lead the blind.
   Just and holy is thy name,
   I am all unrighteousness;
   false and full of sin I am,
   thou art full of truth and grace.

4. Plenteous grace with thee is found,
   grace to cover all my sin;
   let the healing streams abound,
   make and keep me pure within.
   Thou of life the fountain art;
   freely let me take of thee;
   spring thou up within my heart,
   rise to all eternity.

839 Jesus, the joy of loving hearts

Words: attributed to St Bernard of Clairvaux
trans. Ray Palmer, revised and adapted by
Graham Kendrick

Music: Graham Kendrick
arr. Richard Lewis

Last time

light. Chase the dark night of sin a-

way, bathe all the world in ho-ly light.

2. Your truth unchanged has ever stood,
   you rescue those who on you call.
   To those who seek, you're always good,
   to those who find you, all in all.
   To those who seek, you're always good,
   to those who find you, all in all.

3. We taste of you, O living bread,
   and long to feast upon you still.
   We drink of you, the fountain head,
   here may our thirsty souls be filled.
   We drink of you, the fountain head,
   here may our thirsty souls be filled.

4. Our restless spirits yearn for you
   through changing scenes, uncertain paths;
   glad when your smile of grace we see,
   happy when faith can hold you fast;
   glad when your smile of grace we see,
   happy when faith can hold you fast.

5. O Jesus, ever with us stay,
   your presence here so calm and bright.
   Chase the dark night of sin away,
   bathe all the world in holy light.
   Chase the dark night of sin away,
   bathe all the world in holy light.
   Chase the dark night of sin away,
   bathe all the world in holy light.

840 Jesus, there's no one like you

Words and Music: Wes Sutton

Je - sus, there's no one like you. Je - sus, no one

loves like you do. Je - sus, the glo - ry of God,

no one com - pares with you. Je - sus, the

Fa - ther's de - light, Je - sus, the world's bright-est light.

Je - sus, I want you to know that all that I want is

you. All that I want is you.

Who may ascend the hill of the Lord?
Who may stand in his holy place?
He who has clean hands and a pure heart.

Psalm 24:3, 4a

841 Jesus, thy blood and righteousness

Words: Nicolaus Ludwig von Zinzendorf
trans. John Wesley

Music: William Smallwood

ANTWERP LM

1. Jesus, thy blood and righteousness my beauty are, my glorious dress; midst flaming worlds, in these arrayed, with joy shall I lift up my head.

2. Bold shall I stand in thy great day;
   for to my charge who aught shall lay?
   Fully absolved through these I am,
   from sin and fear, from guilt and shame.

3. That holy, meek, unspotted Lamb,
   who from the Father's bosom came,
   who suffered for me, to atone,
   now for my Lord and God I own.

4. Lord, I believe thy precious blood,
   which at the mercy-seat of God
   for ever doth for sinners plead,
   for me, e'en for my soul, was shed.

5. When from the dust of death I rise
   to claim my mansion in the skies,
   e'en then this shall be all my plea—
   Jesus hath lived, hath died for me!

842 Jesus, we have heard your Spirit
(Where you lead us)

Words: Martin E. Leckebusch

Music: *Ode to Joy,* Ludwig van Beethoven
arr. Christopher Tambling

where you lead us, we will fol - low

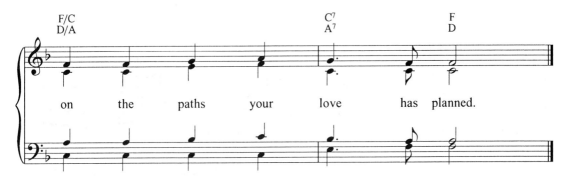

on the paths your love has planned.

2. As a chosen, pilgrim people
   we are learning day by day
   what it means to be disciples,
   to believe and to obey.
   Word and table show your purpose;
   hearts and lives we gladly bring—
   where you lead us, we will follow,
   suff'ring Saviour, risen King.

3. How we yearn that ev'ry people
   should exalt your matchless name,
   yet so often this world's systems
   countermand your regal claim.
   If we stand for truth and justice
   we, like you, may suffer loss;
   where you lead us, we will follow—
   give us grace to bear our cross.

4. So we journey on together,
   keen to make our calling sure;
   through our joys, our fears, our crises,
   may our faith be made mature.
   Jesus, hope of hearts and nations,
   Sov'reign Lord of time and space,
   where you lead us, we will follow
   till we see you face to face.

843 Jesus, what a wonder you are

Words and Music: Richard Lewis

O, how I long to see your face,

beau-ti - ful Sa - viour, King of grace.

There is such peace in your em - brace:

Je - sus, what a won-der you are.

2. Jesus, what a wonder you are;
   no greater love can be found
   than you gave your life for me:
   O what a friend and guide!
   Jesus, what a wonder you are;
   you carried all of my sorrows and shame
   there on the cross:
   O what a friend and guide!

When Jesus spoke again to the people,
he said, 'I am the light of the world.
Whoever follows me will never walk in darkness,
but will have the light of life.'

John 8:12

844 Jesus, where'er thy people meet

Words: William Cowper

Music: William Knapp

WAREHAM LM

1. Jesus, where-'er thy people meet, there they behold thy mer-cy-seat; where-'er they seek thee thou art found, and ev-'ry place is hal-lowed ground.

2. For thou, within no walls confined,
   inhabitest the humble mind;
   such ever bring thee when they come,
   and, going, take thee to their home.

3. Dear Shepherd of thy chosen few,
   thy former mercies here renew;
   here to our waiting hearts proclaim
   the sweetness of thy saving name.

4. Here may we prove the pow'r of prayer
   to strengthen faith and sweeten care,
   to teach our faint desires to rise,
   and bring all heav'n before our eyes.

5. Lord, we are few, but thou art near;
   nor short thine arm, nor deaf thine ear;
   O rend the heav'ns, come quickly down,
   and make a thousand hearts thine own.

845 Jesus, you are Lord of heaven *(You are so good)*

Words and Music: Paul Banderet
arr. Richard Lewis

1. Je - sus, you are Lord of hea - ven

yet to earth you glad - ly came.

Be - cause you gave your life up for me

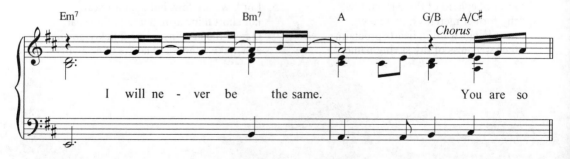

I will ne - ver be the same. You are so

good, you are so won-der-ful. How I

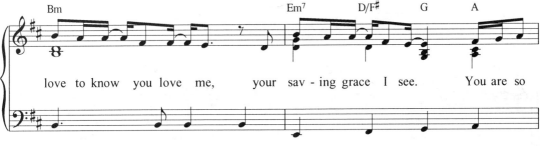

love to know you love me, your sav - ing grace I see. You are so

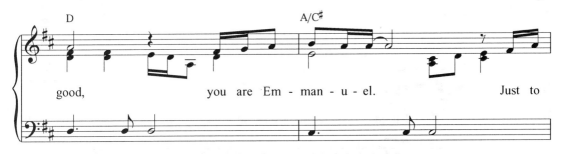

good, you are Em - man - u - el. Just to

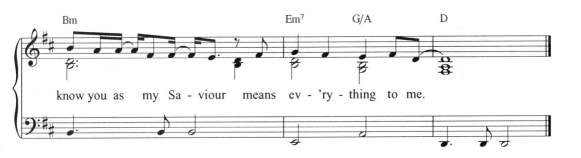

know you as my Sa - viour means ev - 'ry - thing to me.

2. Jesus, I have come to wonder
   at the beauty of your name.
   And as I live each moment for you
   I will never be the same.

846 Jesus, you're all I need

Words and Music: Darlene Zschech

The Spirit of the Sovereign Lord is on me,
because the Lord has anointed me
to preach good news to the poor.
He has sent me to bind up the broken-hearted,
to proclaim freedom for the captives
and release from darkness for the prisoners,
to proclaim the year of the Lord's favour
and the day of vengeance of our God,
to comfort all who mourn,
and provide for those who grieve in Zion –
to bestow on them a crown of beauty instead of ashes,
the oil of gladness instead of mourning,
and a garment of praise instead of a spirit of despair.

Isaiah 61:1-3a

847 Jesus, you're the sweetest name of all
(The sweetest name of all)

Words and Music: Tommy Coomes
arr. Chris Mitchell

1. Je - sus, you're the sweet - est name of all;

Je - sus, you al - ways hear me when I call. O Je - sus, you pick me

up each time I fall; you're the sweet - est, the sweet-est name of all.

2. Jesus, how I love to praise your name;
   Jesus, you're still the first, the last, the same.
   O Jesus, you died and took away my shame;
   you're the sweetest, the sweetest name of all.

3. Jesus, you're the soon and coming King;
   Jesus, we need the love that you can bring.
   O Jesus, we lift our voices up and sing;
   you're the sweetest, the sweetest name of all.

848 Join all the glorious names

Words: Isaac Watts, adapted by Bob Kauflin

Music: Bob Kauflin

1. Join all the glor-ious names of wis-dom, love and pow'r that mor-tals e-ver knew, that an-gels e-ver bore; all are too poor to speak your vast and price-less worth, too poor to set my Sa-viour forth.

Chorus Je-sus, your name is glo-ri-ous, our

Pro - phet, Priest and King. Je - sus, you're reign-ing o-ver us and for e-ver - more your prai - ses we will sing.

To verses 2 & 3

Last time

2. Great
3. Je -

2. Great Prophet of my God,
   my tongue would bless your name,
   through you the joyful news of our salvation came.
   The long-awaited news
   of ev'ry sin forgiv'n,
   of hell subdued and peace with heav'n.

3. Jesus, my great high Priest,
   you shed your blood and died,
   my guilty conscience seeks no sacrifice beside.
   Your pure and precious blood
   for all my sin atoned,
   and now it pleads before the throne.

849 Joyful, joyful, we adore thee

Words: Henry van Dyke

Music: Ludwig van Beethoven
adapted by Edward Hodges

ODE TO JOY 87 87 D

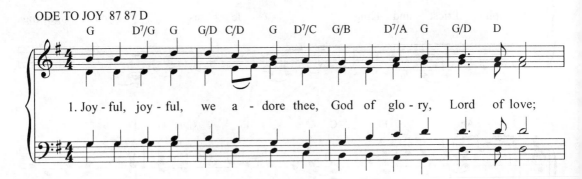

1. Joy-ful, joy-ful, we a-dore thee, God of glo-ry, Lord of love;

hearts un-fold like flow'rs be-fore thee, op'n-ing to the sun a-bove.

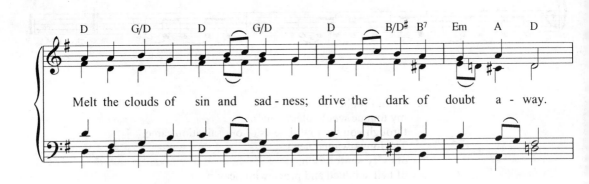

Melt the clouds of sin and sad-ness; drive the dark of doubt a-way.

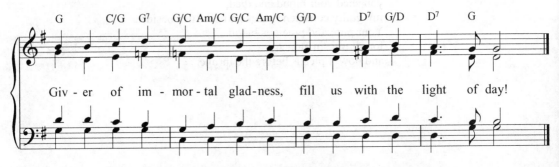

Giv-er of im-mor-tal glad-ness, fill us with the light of day!

2. All thy works with joy surround thee,
   earth and heav'n reflect thy rays.
   Stars and angels sing around thee,
   centre of unbroken praise.
   Field and forest, vale and mountain,
   flow'ry meadow, flashing sea,
   chanting bird and flowing fountain
   call us to rejoice in thee!

3. Thou art giving and forgiving,
   ever blessing, ever blest,
   wellspring of the joy of living,
   ocean depth of happy rest!
   Thou our Father, Christ our brother,
   all who live in love are thine.
   Teach us how to love each other;
   lift us to the joy divine!

4. Mortals, join the mighty chorus
   which the morning stars began;
   love divine is reigning o'er us,
   leading us with mercy's hand.
   Ever singing, march we onward,
   victors in the midst of strife.
   Joyful music leads us sunward
   in the triumph-song of life!

850 Just let me say

Words and Music: Geoff Bullock

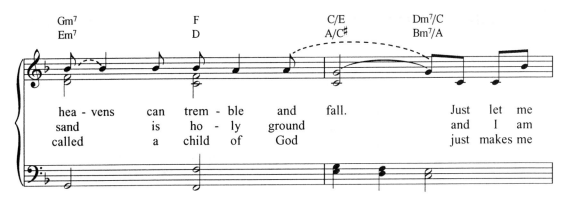

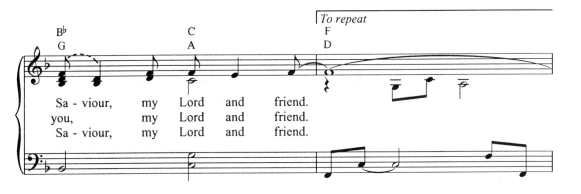

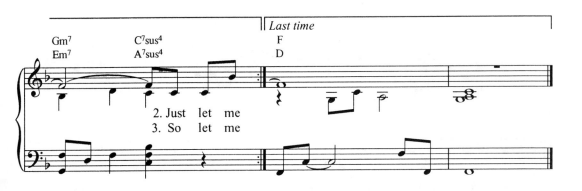

851 Lamp unto my feet

(It is you)

Words and Music: Darlene Zschech

1. Lamp un-to my feet, light un-to my path. It is

you, Je-sus, it is you.

2. This

trea - sure that I hold, more than fin-est gold. It is
(v.3) take my bro-ken-ness, call me to your-self, there you

you, Je-sus, it is you.
stand, heal-ing in your hands.

Chorus

With all my heart, with all my soul, I live to wor - ship you and praise

for e - ver-more, praise for e - ver-more.

Lord ev - 'ry day I need you more, on wings of hea - ven I will soar

1.

with you.

D.S. Last time

3. You

852 Lead me, Lord

Words and Music: James Lewis

As I rise, to when I sleep, I will praise you.

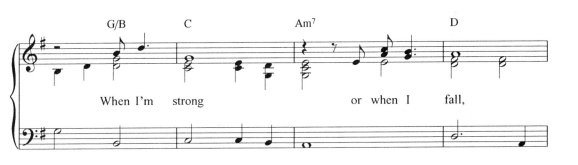

When I'm strong or when I fall,

Lord, let me praise you. Lord, let me praise you

and as I wor - ship you, lead me, Lord.

853 Lead me on

(Without you)

Words ands Music: Mark Naea, Vernon Katipa
and Frank Kereopa arr. Chris Mitchell

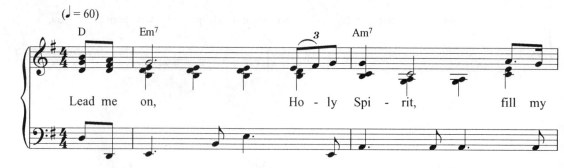

Lead me on, Ho - ly Spi - rit, fill my

heart, come flood my soul; lead me on, in - to your

pre - sence, touch me, Lord Je - sus, I need you.

I can't live with - out you, I can't walk this

road   a-lone;   in my heart   I   need   you,

Ho-ly One,   come take my   hand.

854 Let everything that has breath

Words and Music: Matt Redman

2. Praise you in the heavens,
joining with the angels,
joining you for ever and a day.
Praise you on the earth now,
joining with creation,
calling all the nations to your praise.
If they could see . . .

855 Let everything that isn't pure   *(Pure and holy)*

Words and Music: Jamie Burgess
arr. Chris Mitchell

1. Let ev-'ry-thing that is-n't pure in your sight, Lord Je-sus,
be swept a-way by your pow-er, Lord.
I want to stand be-fore you dressed in the fin-est lin-en:
ho-ly, in pu-ri-ty, my Lord.

Chorus

Pure and ho-ly,

giv - ing glo - ry to the King of kings.

Here, be - fore you, I a - dore you, prai - ses I will bring.

Last time

D.C.

2. I set my eyes upon you,
   I focus my mind on you,
   I want to give you, oh, so much.
   Touch me and move my spirit,
   love me without a limit.
   Oh Lord, I cry out for your touch.

856 Let my heart be the temple of your Spirit
(Fill this temple)

Words and Music: Jim Cernero
arr. Richard Lewis

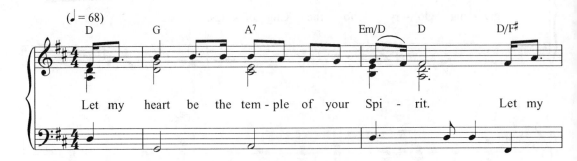

Let my heart be the tem - ple of your Spi - rit. Let my

spi - rit feel the warmth of your em - brace. Let me

be a ho - ly ha - bi - ta - tion where your

Spi - rit is pleased to dwell. Oh Lord, I long to know your

glo - ry.   I   want   to   of - fer   the   sac - ri - fice   of

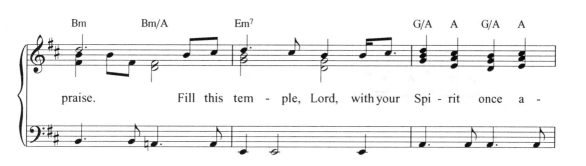

praise.   Fill   this   tem - ple, Lord, with your   Spi - rit   once   a -

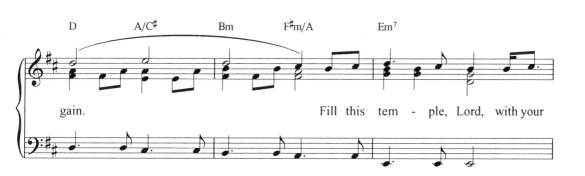

gain.   Fill   this   tem - ple, Lord,   with your

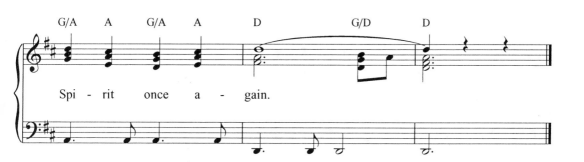

Spi - rit   once   a - gain.

857 Let the chimes of freedom ring

(Chimes of freedom)

Words and Music: Dave Bilbrough

With a lilting feel

Verse

1. Let the chimes of free-dom ring all a-cross the earth; lift your voice in praise to him and sing of all his worth, and sing of all his worth.

live. Let all the peo-ple hear the news of the One who comes to save: he's the Lord of all the

2. Open wide your prison doors
   to greet the Lord of life;
   songs of triumph fill the air,
   Christ Jesus is alive,
   Christ Jesus is alive.

3. In ev'ry corner of the earth
   to ev'ry tribe and tongue,
   make known that God so loved this world
   that he gave his only Son,
   he gave his only Son.

4. Spread the news and make it plain:
   he breaks the pow'r of sin.
   Jesus died and rose again,
   his love will never end,
   his love will never end.

5. He will return in majesty
   to take his rightful place
   as King of all eternity,
   the Name above all names,
   the Name above all names.

858 Let the heavens rejoice *(Rise up and praise him)*

Words and Music: Paul Baloche and Gary Sadler

Let the hea-vens re-joice, let the earth be glad; let the peo-ple of God sing his praise all o-ver the land. Ev-'ry-one in the val-ley, come, and lift your voice; all those on the moun-tain top be glad and shout for joy.

Chorus Rise up and praise him, he de-serves our love;

Create in me a pure heart, O God,
and renew a steadfast spirit within me.

Psalm 51:10

859 Let the poor man say (Let the river flow)

Words and Music: Darrell Evans

Ho - ly Spi - rit, come,

move in pow - er. Let the ri - ver flow, let the

ri - ver flow, let the ri - ver flow.

860 Let there be praise

Words and Music: Dick and Melodie Tunney

1. Let there be praise, let there be joy in our hearts.
2. Let there be praise, let there be joy in our hearts.

Sing to the Lord, give him the glo - ry;
For e - ver - more let his love

(glo - ry); fill the air and let there be praise.

861 Let the same mind *(God has exalted him)*

Words and Music: Graham Kendrick

862 Let the weak say 'I am strong'
(What the Lord has done in me)

Words and Music: Reuben Morgan
arr. Chris Mitchell

1. Let the weak say 'I am strong', let the poor say 'I am rich', let the blind say 'I can see, it's what the Lord has done in me'. Let the

Chorus

Ho - sanna, ho - sanna to the Lamb that was slain! Ho - sanna, ho - sanna! Je - sus died and rose a-gain! Ho - sanna, ho -

Let us acknowledge the Lord;
let us press on to acknowledge him.
As surely as the sun rises,
he will appear;
he will come to us like the winter rains,
like the spring rains that water the earth.

Hosea 6:3

863 Let your glory fall

Words and Music: Don Moen

2. Ev'ry tongue and tribe gathered 'round your throne;
   with one voice we cry, 'Holy Lord.'
   Ev'ry tongue and tribe, ev'ry tongue and tribe,
   ev'ry tongue and tribe.

3. Glory to the Lamb, Lamb upon the throne;
   all the saints proclaim, 'Jesus reigns.'
   Glory to the Lamb, glory to the Lamb,
   glory to the Lamb.

864 Lift up your heads

Words and Music: Tommy Walker
arr. Chris Mitchell

1. Lift up your heads (lift up your heads), O you gates
2. Lift up your hands (lift up your hands), o-pen up your hearts

(O you gates); swing o-pen wide (swing o-pen wide),
(o-pen up your hearts); his vic-t'ry o-ver sin (his vic-t'ry o-ver sin)

you an-cient doors (you an-cient doors); let the King of kings
and death is ours (and death is ours);

Praise him with the sounding of the trumpet,
praise him with the harp and lyre,
praise him with tambourine and dancing,
praise him with the strings and flute,
praise him with the clash of cymbals,
praise him with resounding cymbals.

Psalm 150:3-5

865 Lift up your heads, O you gates

Words and Music: Richard Lewis

866 Like a river glorious

Words: Frances Ridley Havergal

Music: J. Mountain

WYE VALLEY 65 65 and Refrain

1. Like a river glorious is God's perfect peace,
o - ver all vic - tor - ious, in its bright in - crease:
per - fect, yet it flow - eth full - er ev - 'ry day;
per - fect, yet it grow - eth deep - er all the way.

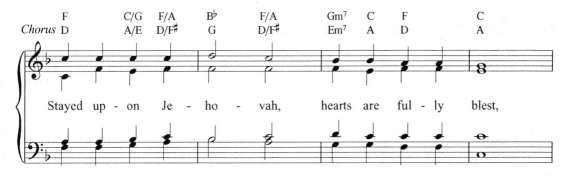

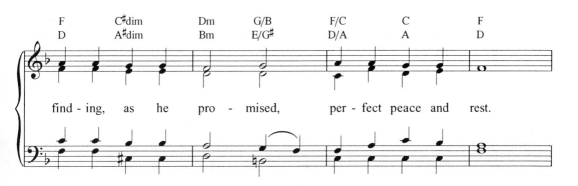

2. Hidden in the hollow of his blessèd hand,
   never foe can follow, never traitor stand;
   not a surge of worry, not a shade of care,
   not a blast of hurry touched the Spirit there.
   Stayed upon Jehovah . . .

3. Ev'ry joy or trial falleth from above,
   traced upon our dial by the sun of love.
   We may trust him fully, all for us to do;
   they who trust him wholly find him wholly true.
   Stayed upon Jehovah . . .

867 Long ago, prophets knew

Words: Fred Pratt Green

Music: From *Piae Cantiones*
arr. Richard Lloyd

PERSONENT HODIE (THEODORIC) 666 66 and Refrain

1. Long a-go, pro-phets knew Christ would come, born a Jew,

come to make all things new, bear his peo-ple's bur-den,

Chorus

free-ly love and par-don. Ring, bells, ring, ring, ring!

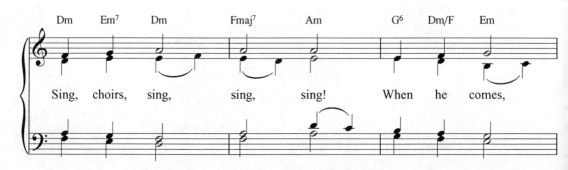

Sing, choirs, sing, sing, sing! When he comes,

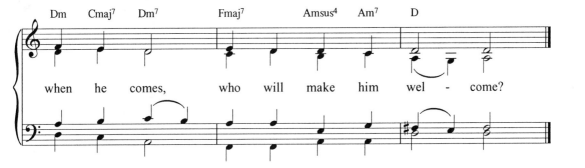

when he comes, who will make him wel - come?

2. God in time, God in man,
   this is God's timeless plan:
   he will come, as a man,
   born himself of woman,
   God divinely human.

3. Mary, hail! Though afraid,
   she believed, she obeyed.
   In her womb, God is laid:
   till the time expected,
   nurtured and protected.

4. Journey ends! Where afar
   Bethlem shines, like a star,
   stable door stands ajar.
   Unborn Son of Mary,
   Saviour, do not tarry!

Therefore, if anyone is in Christ,
he is a new creation;
the old has gone, the new has come!

2 Corinthians 5:17

868 Look what you've done in my life   *(Your love)*

Words and Music: Eoghan Heaslip and Mick Goss

Look what you've done in my life,
see what you've done in this heart,
you've brought hope, heal-ing and free-dom,
look what you've done in my life.

-sus, you came to pay my ran - som, it's

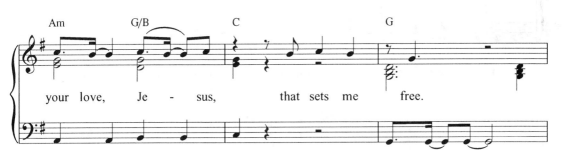

your love, Je - sus, that sets me free.

869 Look, ye saints

Words: Thomas Kelly

Music: Henry Smart

REGENT SQUARE 87 87 87

2. Crown the Saviour! Angels, crown him!
   Rich the trophies Jesus brings;
   in the seat of pow'r enthrone him,
   while the vault of heaven rings:
   Crown him, crown him!
   Crown him, crown him!
   Crown the Saviour King of kings!

3. Sinners in derision crowned him,
   mocking thus the Saviour's claim;
   saints and angels crowd around him,
   own his title, praise his name:
   Crown him, crown him!
   Crown him, crown him!
   Spread abroad the Victor's fame.

4. Hark, those bursts of acclamation!
   Hark, those loud triumphant chords!
   Jesus takes the highest station:
   O what joy the sight affords!
   Crown him, crown him!
   Crown him, crown him!
   King of kings and Lord of lords!

870 Lord, enthroned in heavenly splendour

Words: George Hugh Bourne

Music: George Clement Martin

* Optional notes for accompanist

2. Here our humblest homage pay we,
   here in loving rev'rence bow;
   here in faith's discernment pray we,
   lest we fail to know thee now.
   Alleluia, alleluia,
   thou art here, we ask not how.

3. Though the lowliest form doth veil thee
   as of old in Bethlehem,
   here as there thine angels hail thee,
   Branch and Flow'r of Jesse's Stem.
   Alleluia, alleluia,
   we in worship join with them.

4. Paschal Lamb, thine off'ring, finished
   once for all when thou wast slain,
   in its fullness undiminished
   shall for evermore remain.
   Alleluia, alleluia,
   cleansing souls from ev'ry stain.

5. Life-imparting heav'nly manna,
   stricken rock with streaming side,
   heav'n and earth with loud hosanna
   worship thee, the Lamb who died.
   Alleluia, alleluia,
   ris'n, ascended, glorified!

871 Lord, how you came and rescued me *(I love you)*

Words and Music: Clive Goodwill
arr. Chris Mitchell

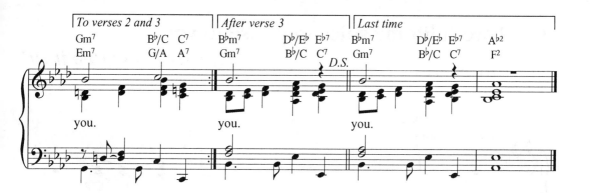

2. Lord, how you gave yourself for me,
   hung upon that cursèd tree;
   I'm ever thankful to you.
   You, how you've shown me your great love,
   even now you're praying above
   that I would always love you.

3. Lord, help me do your will today,
   hear you, trust you, then obey,
   so I may always please you.
   Lord, how your love will draw me on
   'til all trace of self is gone
   and I'll be yours completely.

872 Lord, I lift my voice in praise to you
(Jesus, you gave it all)

Words and Music: Craig Gower

and your grace

brings

pow'r to set this sin - ner free, and your blood

pours joy in - to my life; Je - sus, you gave

To repeat

it all for me. 1. Lord, I

Last time

for me.

2. And with ev'ry breath that comes from me
will flow your mercy and your grace,
proclaiming love and liberty,
for all who have an ear to hear.

873 Lord, I long to see you glorified

(Lord of all)

Words and Music: Steve McPherson

God, who has called you into fellowship
with his Son Jesus Christ our Lord, is faithful.

1 Corinthians 1:9

874 Lord Jesus Christ, we seek thy face

Words: Lowell Mason

Music: Alexander Stewart
arr. Alan Cunningham

2. We thank thee for the precious blood
   that purged our sins and brought us nigh.
   All cleansed and sanctified to God,
   thy holy name to magnify.

3. The brow that once with thorns was bound,
   thy hands, thy side we fain would see;
   draw near, Lord Jesus, glory crowned,
   and bless us while we wait on thee.

875 Lord, my heart before you
(Honest heart)

Words and Music: Trish Morgan

Lord, my heart be-fore you is o-pen and bare.
I stand in need of your mer - cy, in need of your
care. Wash my sins a -
way in this fall - ing rain. In this

The Son is the radiance of God's glory
and the exact representation of his being,
sustaining all things by his powerful word.

Hebrews 1:3a

876 Lord of glory, we adore you

Words: R. Holden
revised and adapted by Graham Kendrick

Music: Henry John Gauntlett

IRBY 87 87 77

1. Lord of glory, we adore you, Christ of God, ascended high. Heart and soul we bow before you, glorious now beyond the sky. You we worship, you we praise; excellent in all your ways.

2. Mighty King in heav'n exalted,
   rightful heir and Lord of all,
   once despised, disowned, rejected
   by the ones you came to call;
   you we honour, you adore,
   glorious now and evermore.

3. Lord of life, to death made subject,
   blesser, yet a curse once-made
   of your Father's heart the object,
   yet in depths of anguish laid;
   you we gaze on, you recall,
   bearing here our sorrows all.

877 Lord of hosts

Words and Music: Janine Price
arr. Dave Bankhead

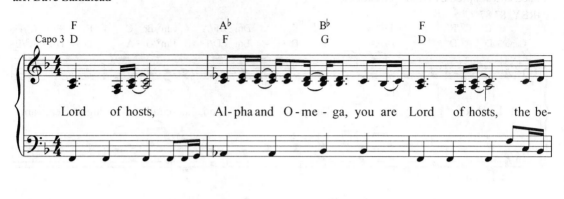

Lord of hosts, Al-pha and O-me-ga, you are Lord of hosts, the be-

gin-ning and the end, you reign on high.

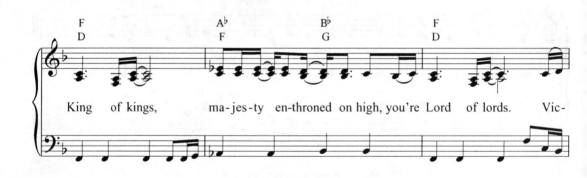

King of kings, ma-jes-ty en-throned on high, you're Lord of lords. Vic-

to-ri-ous o-ver sin and death. And I

878 Lord of the heavens

Words and Music: Shaun and Mel Griffiths
arr. Chris Mitchell

Lord of the hea - vens, I bow my knee and wor - ship you, I stand be-fore you and I am a - mazed, I see your beau - ty dis-played in ev - 'ry - thing you do. For you are my Sa - viour, Lord

879 Lord, we come before your throne

(We will worship you)

Words and Music: Scott Wesley Brown
arr. Richard Lewis

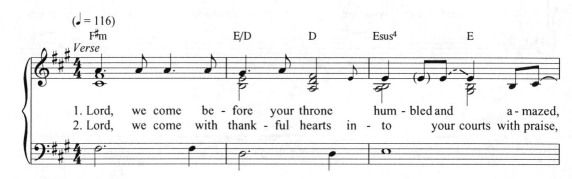

1. Lord, we come be-fore your throne hum-bled and a-mazed,
2. Lord, we come with thank-ful hearts in-to your courts with praise,

your great-ness o-ver-shad-ows ev-'ry
re-joic-ing in your fa-vour, de-

i-dol of this age; for all the trea-sures of this world,
light-ing in your ways; for all we've lost can-not com-pare,

Lord, can-not re-place the great-est joy of know-
Lord, to what we've gained, for there is none like you,

880 Lord, we turn to you and pray

Words and Music: Eoghan Heaslip, Mick Goss and Becky Heaslip

'Father, glorify your name!'
Then a voice came from heaven,
'I have glorified it, and will glorify it again.'

John 12:28

881 Lord, we've come to worship

Words and Music: Tommy Coombes and Don Moen
arr. Chris Mitchell

1. Lord, we've come to wor - ship, and we have come to pray;
2. Lord, we need for - give - ness, we've wan - dered far a - way;

Lord, we've come to lis - ten, and
look down in ten - der mer - cy, for -

hear what you would say; O
give our sins, we pray; O

Lord, our hearts are long - ing to meet with you to - day; for
Lord, we need re - viv - al, all a - cross this land; come

we have come to seek you, and we have come to say:
move a-mong your peo - ple, with your migh - ty hand.

Chorus

Wor - thy, you are wor - thy, King of kings, Lord of lords, you are wor - thy. All bles - sing and pow - er, all rich - es and wis - dom, all glo - ry and hon - our and praise to the Lamb.

882 Lord, you've been good to me

Words and Music: Graham Kendrick
arr. Richard Lewis

1. Lord, you've been good to me all my life,
2. So may each breath I take be for you, Lord,

all my life; your lov - ing kind - ness ne - ver fails.
on - ly you, giv - ing you back the life I owe.

I will re -
Love so a -

mem - ber all you have done, bring from my
maz - ing, mer - cy so free, Lord, you've been

883 Loved with everlasting love

Words: George Wade Robinson

Music: J Mountain

I AM HIS 77 77 D

1. Loved with e - ver-last-ing love, led by grace that love to know; Spi - rit

breath - ing from a - bove, thou hast taught me it is so. O this

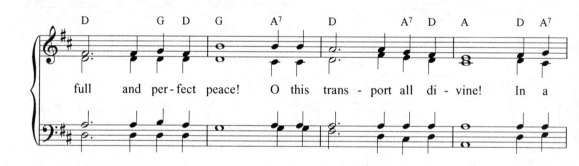

full and per-fect peace! O this trans - port all di - vine! In a

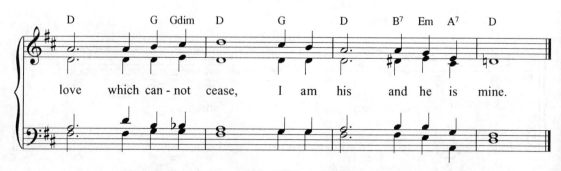

love which can-not cease, I am his and he is mine.

2. Heaven above is softer blue,
   earth around is sweeter green;
   something lives in every hue
   Christless eyes have never seen;
   birds with gladder songs o'erflow,
   flowers with deeper beauties shine,
   since I know, as now I know,
   I am his, and he is mine.

3. Things that once were wild alarms
   cannot now disturb my rest;
   closed in everlasting arms,
   pillowed on the loving breast.
   O to lie for ever here,
   doubt and care and self resign,
   while he whispers in my ear,
   I am his and he is mine.

4. His for ever, only his;
   who the Lord and me shall part?
   Ah, with what a rest of bliss
   Christ can fill the loving heart!
   Heaven and earth may fade and flee;
   firstborn light in gloom decline;
   but, while God and I shall be,
   I am his, and he is mine.

884 Love songs from heaven

Words and Music: Noel and Tricia Richards

With strength

1. Love songs from hea - ven are fill - ing the earth,

bring - ing great hope to all na - tions;

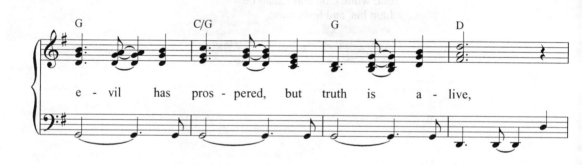

e - vil has pros - pered, but truth is a - live,

in this dark world the light still shines.

D.C. for verse 2

Chorus

For you we live, and for you we may die,
through us may Je - sus be seen;
for you a - lone we will of - fer our lives,
in this dark world our light will shine.

2. Nothing has silenced this gospel of Christ,
   it echoes down through the ages.
   Blood of the martyrs has made your Church strong,
   in this dark world the light still shines.

3. Let ev'ry nation be filled with your song;
   this is the cry of your people,
   'We will not settle for anything less,
   in this dark world our light must shine.'

885 Many waters cannot quench your love

(Holy love)

Words and Music: Andy Park

1. Ma-ny wa-ters can-not quench your love,
2. Ma-ny sor-rows can-not quench your love,

ri-vers can-not o-ver-whelm it.
dark-ness can-not o-ver-whelm it.

O-ceans of fear can-not con-ceal your
I will not fear, your love is here to

love for me.
com-fort me.

I will proclaim the name of the Lord.
Oh, praise the greatness of our God!
He is the Rock, his works are perfect,
and all his ways are just.
A faithful God who does no wrong,
upright and just is he.

Deuteronomy 32:3-4

886 May our homes be filled with dancing

(Hear our praises)

Words and Music: Reuben Morgan

1. May our homes be filled with danc - ing,
2. May our light shine in the dark - ness,

may our streets be filled with joy;
as we walk be - fore the cross;

may in-jus - tice bow to Je - sus
may your glo - ry fill the whole earth

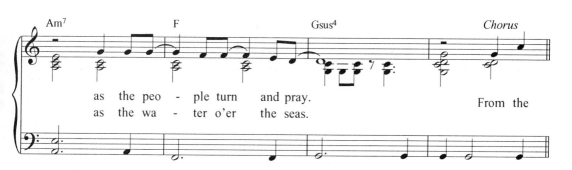

as the peo - ple turn and pray.
as the wa - ter o'er the seas.

From the

moun - tain   to   the   val - ley,   hear our   prai - ses

rise   to   you.   From   the   hea - vens

to   the   na - tions,   hear   our   sing - ing

Last time to Coda **1, 3.**

fill   the   air.

In him the whole building is joined together
and rises to become a holy temple in the Lord.
And in him you too are being built together
to become a dwelling in which God lives by his Spirit.

Ephesians 2:21-22

887 May the mind of Christ my Saviour

Words: Katie Barclay Wilkinson

Music: A. Cyril Barham-Gould

ST. LEONARDS 87 85

1. May the mind of Christ my Saviour live in me from day to day, by his love and pow'r con-trol-ling all I do and say.

2. May the word of God dwell richly
   in my heart from hour to hour,
   so that all may see I triumph
   only through his pow'r.

3. May the peace of God my Father
   rule my life in ev'rything,
   that I may be calm to comfort
   sick and sorrowing.

4. May the love of Jesus fill me,
   as the waters fill the sea;
   him exalting, self abasing,
   this is victory.

5. May I run the race before me,
   strong and brave to face the foe,
   looking only unto Jesus
   as I onward go.

6. May his beauty rest upon me
   as I seek the lost to win,
   and may they forget the channel,
   seeing only him.

888 Mercy

Words and Music: Lynn DeShazo and Gary Sadler
arr. Dave Bankhead

2. Lord, you have taught us
   'Love one another'.
   As you have loved us
   so we must love,
   always forbearing,
   always forgiving,
   showing to others
   the mercy we've known.

889 Mercy and love

Words and Music: Chris Orange
arr. Chris Mitchell

you. With my hands raised up to your throne, I will

love, Je - sus, you a - lone. You're my all, my ev - 'ry-thing, my

grace, and I'll live to e - ver sing your praise.

890 More like you

Words and Music: Scott Wesley Brown

2. Lord, you are compassion, and never-ending love,
for you have redeemed me by your precious blood.
Create in me a clean heart, a spirit that is new,
the joy of my salvation is only found in you.

891 More, Lord

(I must have more)

Words and Music: Bryn Haworth
arr. Chris Mitchell

Verse 1 lyrics:
More, Lord, I must have more, Lord, more of your pre-sence, more of your love. For you, Lord, you are the foun-tain of liv-ing wa-ter

Verse 2 lyrics:
More, Lord, I must have more, Lord, more of your Spi-rit flow-ing through me. come, now, come to the wa-ters, all who are thirs-ty

Last time to Coda

that ne - ver runs dry. So
will be sa - tis - fied.

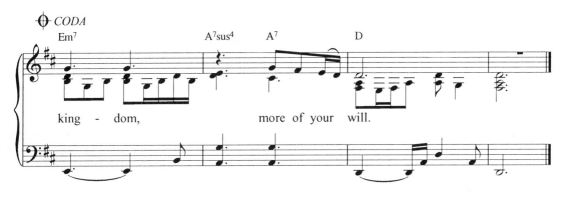

king - dom, more of your will.

892 More, Lord

Words and Music: Richard Lewis

More, Lord, give us more of your Spi-rit, give us more; we o-pen our hearts. More, Lord, give us more of your Spi-rit in our lives; we yield them to you. Give us more of your Spi-rit, give us more of the Son, give us more of the Fa - ther, come and

fill ev - 'ry one. I re - ceive your Spi - rit, I re - ceive your love, I re-

ceive the pow - er of the Lord God a - bove. Glo - ri-

fy your name, glo - ri - fy your name, glo - ri -

fy your name in all the earth. Glo - ri -

893 More than I could hope or dream of *(One day)*

Words and Music: Reuben Morgan

More than I could hope or dream of, you have poured your

fa - vour on me. One day in the house of God is

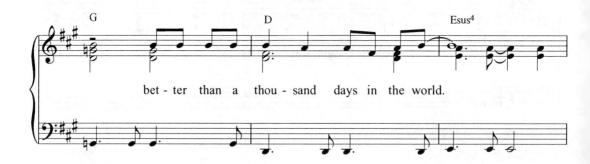

bet - ter than a thou - sand days in the world.

Chorus

So blessed, I can't con - tain it,

894 My eyes be open to your presence *(Open to you)*

Words: Nick and Anita Haigh

Music: traditional melody
arr. Nick and Anita Haigh

1. My eyes be o-pen to your pre-sence, my ears to hear your

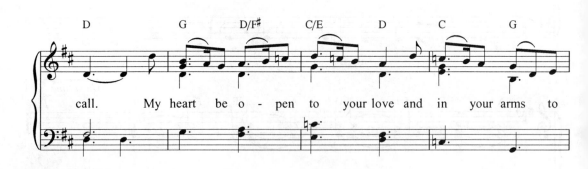

call. My heart be o-pen to your love and in your arms to

fall. My mind be o-pen to your word, my soul to hea-ven's

cure, that I be o-pen to you, Lord, this day and e-ver-

2. My life be open to your leading,
   my hands to do your will.
   My lips be open in your praise
   and for your truth to tell.
   My home be open in your name
   for weary ones and poor,
   that I be open to you, Lord,
   this day and evermore.

3. My door be open to the other
   wherever we may meet.
   My arms be open to the one
   in whom I am complete.
   My self be open to your world
   and in it see your face,
   that I be open to you, Lord,
   held fast in your embrace.

895 My eyes can see your hand (Your love for me)

Words and Music: Don Harris and Gary Sadler
arr. Chris Mitchell

1. My eyes can see your hand at ev-'ry pas-sing glance;
2. I found a deep-er faith with-in your love's em-brace;

your glo-ry co-vers all the earth and sky.
where all I want is what you have for me.

Your good-ness fills my life in ev-'ry cir-cum-stance;
I'm drink-ing from the cup of pure and end-less grace;

my heart is o-pen wide, my hands are lift-ed high.

896 My God, how wonderful thou art

Words: Frederick William Faber

Music: James Turle

WESTMINSTER CM

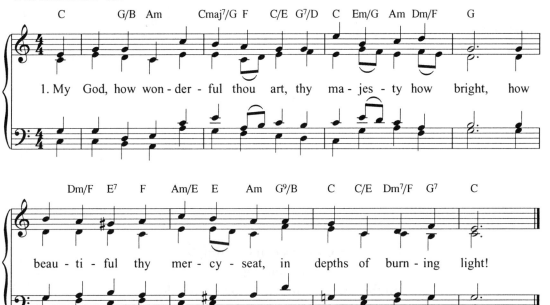

1. My God, how won-der-ful thou art, thy ma-jes-ty how bright, how beau-ti-ful thy mer-cy-seat, in depths of burn-ing light!

2. How dread are thine eternal years,
   O everlasting Lord,
   by prostrate spirits day and night
   incessantly adored!

3. How wonderful, how beautiful,
   the sight of thee must be,
   thine endless wisdom, boundless pow'r,
   and aweful purity!

4. Yet I may love thee too, O Lord,
   almighty as thou art,
   for thou hast stooped to ask of me
   the love of my poor heart.

5. No earthly father loves like thee,
   no mother e'er so mild,
   bears and forebears as thou hast done
   with me thy sinful child.

6. Father of Jesus, love's reward,
   what rapture will it be,
   prostrate before thy throne to lie,
   and gaze and gaze on thee!

For to us a child is born,
to us a son is given,
and the government will be on his shoulders.
And he will be called
Wonderful Counsellor, Mighty God,
Everlasting Father, Prince of Peace.

Isaiah 9:6

897 My song is love unknown

Words: Samuel Crossman

Music: John Ireland

LOVE UNKNOWN 66 66 88

1. My song is love unknown, my Saviour's love to me; love to the loveless shown, that they might lovely be. O who am I, that for my sake my Lord should take frail flesh and die?

2. He came from his blest throne
   salvation to bestow;
   but men made strange, and none
   the longed-for Christ would know:
   but O, my friend,
   my friend indeed,
   who at my need
   his life did spend.

3. Sometimes they strew his way,
   and his sweet praises sing;
   resounding all the day
   hosannas to their King:
   then 'Crucify!'
   is all their breath,
   and for his death
   they thirst and cry.

4. They rise and needs will have,
   my dear Lord made away;
   a murderer they save,
   the Prince of Life they slay;
   yet cheerful he
   to suff'ring goes,
   that he his foes
   from thence might free.

5. Here might I stay and sing,
   no story so divine;
   never was love, dear King!
   Never was grief like thine.
   This is my friend,
   in whose sweet praise
   I all my days
   could gladly spend.

898 Name above all names

Words and Music: Neil Bennetts

Worshipfully

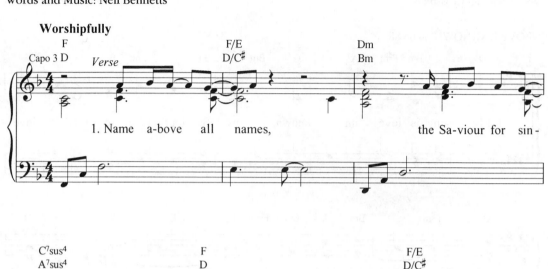

1. Name a-bove all names, the Sa-viour for sin-

- ners slain. You suf-fered for my sake,

to bring me back home a - gain. When I was lost,

you poured your life out for me.

Name a-bove all names, Je-sus, I love you.

2. Giver of mercy,
    the fountain of life for me.
    My spirit is lifted
    to soar on the eagle's wings.
    What love is this
    that fills my heart with treasure?
    Name above all names,
    Jesus, I love you.

3. High King eternal,
    the one true and faithful God.
    The beautiful Saviour,
    still reigning in pow'r and love.
    With all my heart
    I'll worship you for ever:
    Name above all names,
    Jesus, I love you.

899 No eye has seen

(How high and how wide)

Words and Music: Mark Altrogge

1. No eye has seen and no ear has heard and no mind has e - ver con - ceived the glo - ri - ous things that you have pre - pared for ev - 'ry - one who has be - lieved. You brought us near and you called us your own, and

made us joint heirs with your Son. How
high and how wide, how deep and how long, how sweet and how
strong is your love. How la-vish your grace, how
faith-ful your ways, how great is your love, O Lord.

2. Objects of mercy who should have known wrath,
   we're filled with unspeakable joy,
   riches of wisdom, unsearchable wealth
   and the wonder of knowing your voice.
   You are our treasure and our great reward,
   our hope and our glorious king.

Give thanks to the Lord, call on his name;
make known among the nations what he has done,
and proclaim that his name is exalted.
Sing to the Lord, for he has done glorious things;
let this be known to all the world.

Isaiah 12:4-5

900 No one like you

Words and Music: Graham Kendrick
arr. Richard Lewis

1. No one like you, no one like you,
2. No one like you, no one like you,

no one like you, no one like you.
no one like you, no one like you.

(no repeat verse 2)

Beau-ti-ful, won-der-ful, mer-ci-ful, ho-ly,
Son of God, Son of Man, Word of God, ho-ly,

faith-ful, for-giv-ing, God with us.
full of grace, full of truth, God with us.

all glo-ri-ous, mag-ni-fi-cent,
our High Priest in hea-ven

ma - jes - tic, Je - sus.
we wor-ship you, Je - sus.

Je - sus, Je -

sus, God with us.

901 No other prophet

Words: Martin E. Leckebusch

Music: traditional Swiss melody
arr. David Iliff

STAFF OF FAITH 86 86 88 86

Building, with strength

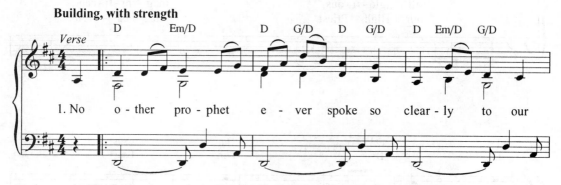

1. No o-ther pro-phet e-ver spoke so clear-ly to our

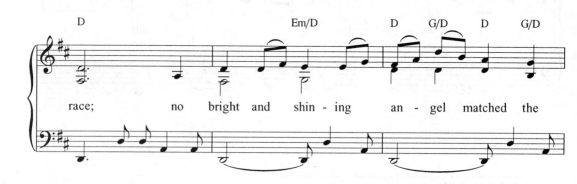

race; no bright and shin-ing an-gel matched the

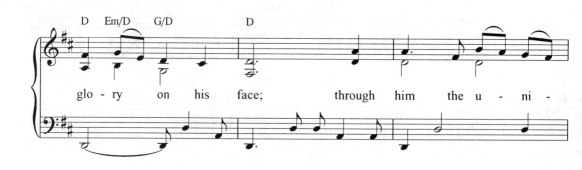

glo-ry on his face; through him the u - ni -

verse was made, by him our debt for sin was paid: in

Christ, at last, we see in full God's splen - dour and God's

To next verse | *Last time*

grace. 2. Ma - might!

2. Majestic angels swiftly fly
   on wings of wind and flame;
   his servants' servants, low they bend
   in honour of his name.
   The Father's precious Son is he,
   the Lord from all eternity:
   yet taking human flesh and blood
   a baby he became.

3. His throne is built on righteousness,
   established firm and sure;
   the oil of joy anoints the one
   who values what is pure!
   The wonder of the Maker's skill
   is seen throughout creation still:
   but when this age has run its course
   his kingdom will endure.

4. God's matchless pow'r confirms that Christ
   is all our life and light;
   his word proclaims the solemn truth
   dividing wrong from right,
   and those who cast that word aside
   are lost like driftwood on the tide:
   but Jesus reigns eternally
   in majesty and might!

902 O come and praise him

Words and Music: Rachel Judd

1. O come and praise him, come on, let's praise him! O come and praise the liv - ing God! O come and praise him, come on, let's praise him! O come and praise the liv - ing God!

Chorus 2:
O, I will praise you, yes, I will praise you!
O, I will praise you for your love.
O, I will praise you, yes, I will praise you!
O, I will praise you for your love.

Verse 2:
Your faithfulness is higher than the mountains,
your faithfulness is deeper than the oceans.
Your faithfulness, it reaches to the heavens,
I will praise you, faithful God!

Chorus 3:
O, I will praise you, yes, I will praise you!
O, I will praise you, faithful God!
O, I will praise you, yes, I will praise you!
O, I will praise you, faithful God!

903 O for a closer walk with God

Words: William Cowper

Music: Charles Hutcheson

STRATHCARO CM

1. O for a clo - ser walk with God, a calm and heav'n - ly frame; a light to shine up - on the road that leads me to the Lamb!

2. Where is the blessedness I knew
   when first I saw the Lord?
   Where is that soul-refreshing view
   of Jesus and his word?

3. What peaceful hours I once enjoyed!
   How sweet their mem'ry still!
   But they have left an aching void
   the world can never fill.

4. Return, O holy Dove! Return,
   sweet messenger of rest!
   I hate the sins that made thee mourn,
   and drove thee from my breast.

5. The dearest idol I have known,
   whate'er that idol be,
   help me to tear it from thy throne.
   And worship only thee.

6. So shall my walk be close with God,
   calm and serene my frame;
   so purer light shall mark the road
   that leads me to the Lamb.

904 O for a heart to praise my God

Words: Charles Wesley

Music: Thomas Wright

STOCKTON CM

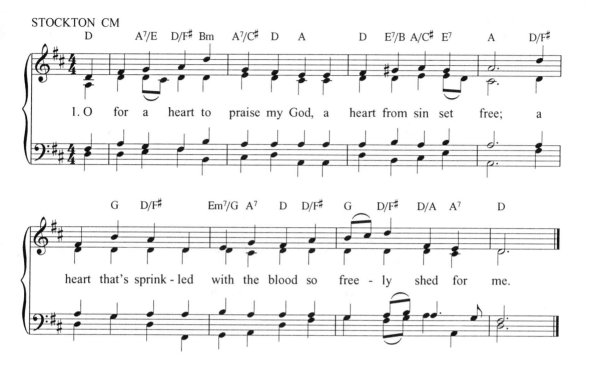

1. O for a heart to praise my God, a heart from sin set free; a heart that's sprink-led with the blood so free-ly shed for me.

2. A heart resigned, submissive, meek,
   my great Redeemer's throne;
   where only Christ is heard to speak,
   where Jesus reigns alone.

3. A humble, lowly, contrite heart,
   believing, true and clean,
   which neither life nor death can part
   from him that dwells within.

4. A heart in ev'ry thought renewed,
   and full of love divine;
   perfect and right and pure and good —
   a copy, Lord, of thine.

5. Thy nature, gracious Lord, impart,
   come quickly from above;
   write thy new name upon my heart,
   thy new best name of love.

905 O God, our help in ages past

Words: Isaac Watts

Music: William Croft

ST ANNE CM

1. O God, our help in a - ges past, our hope for years to come, our shel - ter from the storm - y blast, and our e - ter - nal home.

2. Beneath the shadow of thy throne,
   thy saints have dwelt secure;
   sufficient is thine arm alone,
   and our defence is sure.

3. Before the hills in order stood,
   or earth received her frame,
   from everlasting thou art God,
   to endless years the same.

4. A thousand ages in thy sight
   are like an evening gone;
   short as the watch that ends the night
   before the rising sun.

5. Time, like an ever-rolling stream,
   will bear us all away;
   we fade and vanish, as a dream
   dies at the op'ning day.

6. O God, our help in ages past,
   our hope for years to come,
   be thou our guard while troubles last,
   and our eternal home.

906 O God, you are my God

(Step by step)

Words and Music: Beaker

907 O God, you've been so good to me

(So good to me)

Words and Music: Darrell Evans and Matt Jones
arr. Chris Mitchell

1. O God, you've been so good to me,
   God, you've been so good to me,

you came and found this or - phan and you
and ev - 'ry day I wake up I breathe

brought me right in - to your fa - mi - ly;
an - o - ther breath of your mer - cy;

O God, you've been so good to
O God, you've been so good to

908 O happy day!

Words and Music: unknown
arr. Richard Lewis

2

A/B Amaj⁷/B   E   A

O hap - py day!   (O hap - py day!)   O hap - py day!

E   A

(O   hap - py   day!)   O   hap - py   day!

E   D/A   A   D   A   E

(O hap - py   day!)   O hap - py   day!

909 Oh how great is the Father's love

Words and Music: Matthew Ling

2. Though we cannot comprehend
   your love, O Lord, that never ends,
   yet we know it in our lives today.
   From bursting hearts our songs arise,
   until your praises fill the skies,
   we worship you for evermore.

910 Oh how my spirit rejoices

Words and Music: Wes Sutton

His eyes are e - ver on me

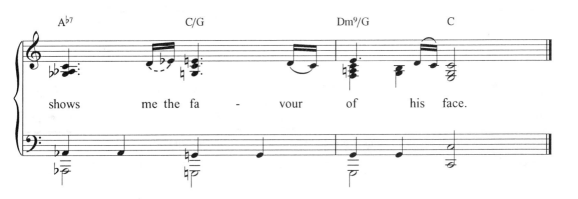

shows me the fa - vour of his face.

2. Oh how my spirit rejoices.
   My soul will glorify,
   the Lord, my God, my Saviour,
   sending his mercy from on high.
   He lifts the broken and humble.
   Proud men, he makes to fall,
   fills hungry hearts with treasures,
   hears the cry of those who call.

3. Oh how my spirit rejoices.
   My soul will glorify,
   the Lord, my God, my Saviour,
   sending his mercy from on high.
   My life will give him glory,
   for all his faithfulness.
   This now the ageless story
   all who call on him are blessed.

911 Oh, kneel me down again

(Humble King)

Words and Music: Brenton Brown
arr. Chris Mitchell

Oh, kneel me down a-gain, here at your feet;
show me how much you love hu-mi-li-ty.
Oh, Spi-rit, be the star that leads me to
the hum-ble heart of love I see in you.
You are the God of the bro-ken, the

912 Oh Lord, you're amazing *(I'm here to worship you)*

Words and Music: Michael Battersby

Oh Lord, you're a-maz-ing, how your love for me will ne-ver end.

Your grace, it sur-rounds me, you're my

Sa-viour, you're my clo-sest friend. Your love's

deep-er than the deep-est sea, I feel it shin-ing like the mid-day sun

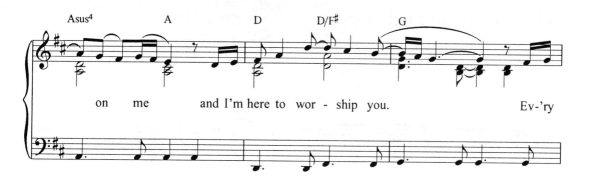

on me   and I'm here to wor - ship you.   Ev-'ry

day that I live   I will live   it for you   and I'm here to wor - ship you.

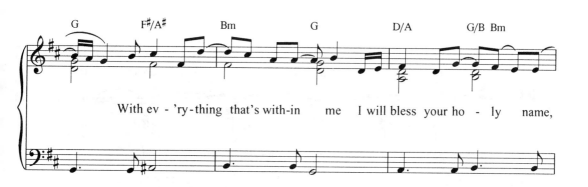

With ev - 'ry-thing that's with-in   me   I will bless your ho - ly   name,

my Em - man - u - el.

913 Oh taste and see

Words and Music: Kevin Simpson
arr. Richard Lewis

Oh taste and see that the Lord is good and his

mer-cies en-dur – eth for e – ver. Oh taste and see that the Lord

To repeat / Last time

is good and his mer-cies en-dur – eth for e – ver. *Fine*

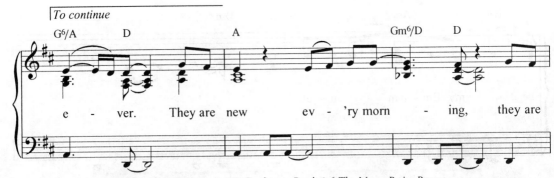

To continue

e – ver. They are new ev – 'ry morn – ing, they are

new ev - 'ry morn - ing, they are new ev - 'ry morn-

- ing; the mer - cies of the Lord.

914 Oh, the mercy of God

Words and Music: Geoff Bullock

Verse

1. Oh, the mer-cy of God, the glo-ry of grace, that you chose to re-deem us, to for-give and re-store, and you call us your child-ren cho-sen in him to be ho-ly and blame-less to the glo-ry of God.

Chorus

To the praise of his glo-ri-ous grace,

to the praise of his glo - ry and power,

to him be all glo - ry, hon - our and praise,

for e - ver and ev - er and e - ver, a - men.

2. Oh, the richness of grace, the depths of his love,
   in him is redemption, the forgiveness of sin.
   You called us as righteous, predestined in him
   for the praise of his glory, included in Christ.

3. Oh, the glory of God expressed in his Son,
   his image and likeness revealed to us all;
   the plea of the ages completed in Christ,
   that we be presented perfected in him.

Praise the Lord.
How good it is to sing praises to our God,
how pleasant and fitting to praise him!

Psalm 147:1

915 O Jesus mine

Words and Music: Marjorie Tancock and Helen Frye
arr. Chris Mitchell

916 O Lord, our Lord *(How majestic is your name)*

Words and Music: Michael W. Smith

Lord, we mag - ni - fy your name; Prince of Peace, Migh - ty God, O Lord God Al -

To repeat　　　　　　*Last time*

migh - ty.　　　　　O ty.

The Lord will surely comfort Zion
and will look with compassion on all her ruins;
he will make her deserts like Eden,
her wastelands like the garden of the Lord.
Joy and gladness will be found in her,
thanksgiving and the sound of singing.

Isaiah 51:3

917 O Love that wilt not let me go

Words: George Matheson

Music: Albert Lister Peace

ST MARGARET 88 88 6

1. O Love that wilt not let me go, I rest my weary soul in thee; I give thee back the life I owe, that in thine ocean depths its flow may richer, fuller be.

2. O Light that follow'st all my way,
   I yield my flick'ring torch to thee;
   my heart restores its borrowed ray,
   that in thy sunshine's blaze its day
   may brighter, fairer be.

3. O Joy that seekest me through pain,
   I cannot close my heart to thee;
   I trace the rainbow through the rain,
   and feel the promise is not vain
   that morn shall tearless be.

4. O Cross that liftest up my head,
   I dare not ask to fly from thee:
   I lay in dust life's glory dead,
   and from the ground there blossoms red
   life that shall endless be.

918 O mystery of love divine!

Words: unknown
revised and adapted by Graham Kendrick

Music: Graham Kendrick
arr. Richard Lewis

1. O mys-te-ry of love di-vine! where right-eous-ness and

peace com-bine and truth and mer-cy meet; God ma-ni-fest in

flesh be-hold, in Je-sus see that love un-fold, the work of grace com-

plete. Love, on-ly love, your heart in-clined and

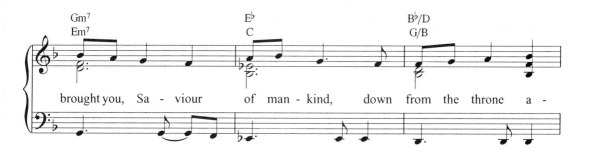

brought you, Sa - viour of man - kind, down from the throne a -

bove; love made you here a Man of Grief, dis - tressed you sore for

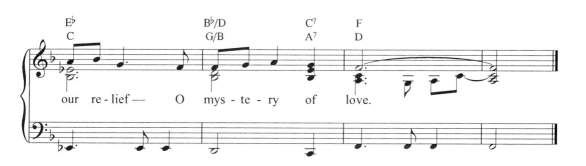

our re - lief — O mys - te - ry of love.

2. Love's glorious triumph now appears
   for you will have your children near
   where grief can never come;
   where ev'ry heart is filled with joy
   and praise shall ev'ry tongue employ
   in love's eternal home.
   Love there will crown what love began,
   its wondrous ways of grace to man
   in its fair home above.
   All, all, O Lord, will there proclaim
   through endless years your blessèd name
   supreme, almighty love.

Will you not revive us again,
that your people may rejoice in you?
Show us your unfailing love, O Lord,
and grant us your salvation.

Psalm 85:6-7

919 One Lord, one faith   *(Increase in me)*

Words and Music: Steve Thompson, Velveta Thompson and Andy Mitchell

1. One Lord, one faith, we stand to-geth-er,

one Lord and Fath - er of us all.

In u - ni-ty and by God's Spi - rit,

we walk as one to reach our goal.

2. To reach the lost is our commission;
   to stretch our hands to those in need.
   Reflect God's heart, fulfil his calling,
   and then his kingdom will increase.

920 One name

(More than treasure)

Words and Music: Johnny Markin

Slowly

1. One name scat-ters my fear, one name brings me to tears when I think of the scars borne for me. One name brings me such peace, one name ne-ver will cease to be held in my heart ten-der-ly.

2. One name to which I'll bow, one name to which I vow to be faith-ful in all that I do. One name, hope for the lost; one name shines from the cross where sal-va-tion is found; one name life made new.

921 Only your mercy, only your grace

Words and Music: Scott Wesley Brown
arr. Richard Lewis

1. Only your mercy, only your grace, only your Spirit brings us to faith; O what a wonder that you chose us first, not by our merit, but your perfect work.

2. Only your goodness, only your love, only your pardon poured out in blood; your righteousness exchanged for our sin, O what a Saviour, O what a friend!

Jesus, we long to worship you, and give you all glory and praise; all that you are, all that you have, we have received by faith.

922 On the blood-stained ground   *(I kneel down)*

Words and Music: Graham Kendrick

1. On the blood-stained ground, where the sha-dow falls,
of a cross and a crown of thorns, I kneel down, I kneel down. I lift my eyes to a tear-stained face, who is this dy-ing in my place? I kneel down, I kneel down.

wash the stains of my guil-ty heart
'til I'm clean in ev-'ry part, I kneel down I kneel down. Wash a-way my shame, my pain, my pride, ev-'ry sin that I once de-nied, I kneel down.

923 On the cross

Words and Music: Geoff Baker

1. On the cross, on the cross, where the King of Glo-ry died, here is grace, here is love, flow-ing from that wound-ed side. A-maz-ing mys-te-ry, that he should die for me, as a

per - fect sa - cri - fice. On the cross, on the

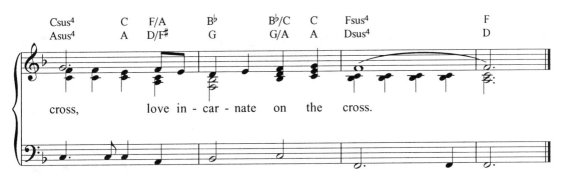

cross, love in - car - nate on the cross.

2. At the cross, at the cross,
all my sin on Jesus laid.
Mine the debt, his the cost,
by his blood the price is paid.
And through his suffering,
that fragrant offering,
arms of love are opened wide.
At the cross, at the cross,
there is healing at the cross.

To the cross, to the cross,
Spirit lead me to the cross.
Bowed in awe at his feet,
richest gain I count as loss.
Nothing compares with this,
to share his righteousness
and be called a child of God.
To the cross, to the cross,
Spirit lead me to the cross.

924 On this assembled host

Words: James Montgomery

Music: Linda Mawson

BEAVERWOOD DSM

1. On this as-sem-bled host, in this ac-cept-ed hour, O Spi-rit, as at Pen-te-cost, des-cend in all your pow'r! We meet with one ac-cord in our ap-point-ed place, and wait the pro-mise of our Lord, the Spi-rit of all grace.

2. Like mighty rushing wind
   upon the waves beneath,
   move with one impulse ev'ry mind;
   one soul, one feeling, breathe.
   Both young and old inspire
   with wisdom from above;
   and give us hearts and tongues of fire,
   to pray and praise and love.

3. Spirit of light, explore
   and chase our gloom away,
   with brightness shining more and more
   until the perfect day.
   Spirit of truth, we pray,
   for ever be our guide;
   O Spirit of adoption, may
   we all be sanctified.

925 O our Lord and King

(King for ever)

Words and Music: Alan Rose

With strength
Chorus

O our Lord and King, our praise to you we bring,

there is no o-ther Rock but you.

Seat - ed high a - bove, you are the one we love,

Fine

this is our song of praise to you.

2. Who else is like you?
    Who else is worthy of your praise?
    We exalt you;
    you reign in majesty and
    awesome splendour,
    king for ever!

3. Abba Father,
    your steadfast love will never fail.
    You are faithful,
    you are God and I will
    worship in your
    courts for ever.

926 Open the eyes of my heart

Words and Music: Paul Baloche

927 O praise the holy Lord above

Words and Music: David Bird, Richard Lacy and Sarah Lacy
arr. Chris Mitchell

1. O praise the ho - ly Lord a - bove, you peo - ple in his tem - ple.
2. Your name, O Lord, and your re - nown en - dure through ge - ne - ra - tions.

Praise him, for the Lord is good and you are his pos - ses - sions. The
You will free your peo - ple, have com - pas - sion on your ser - vants.

Lord a - bove is Lord of all, the earth is here to please him, from
All the na - tions of the earth come to him and praise him.

deep - est sea to clou - dy sky and wind and rain in sea - son.
All of you who fear the Lord, come to him and praise him.

Prais - ing the name of the Lord, prais - ing the
Praise him, the name of the Lord; praise him, the

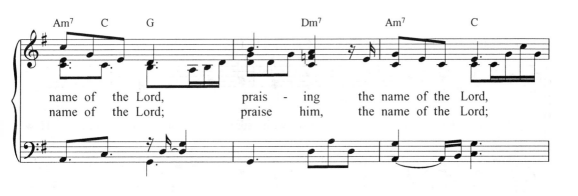

name of the Lord, prais - ing the name of the Lord,
name of the Lord; praise him, the name of the Lord;

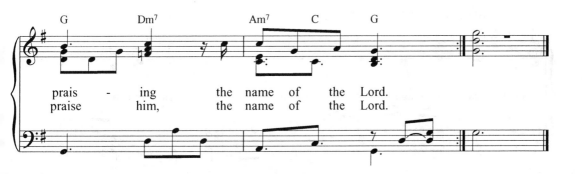

prais - ing the name of the Lord.
praise him, the name of the Lord.

928 O sacred head, once wounded

Words: Paulus Gerhardt attrib. Bernard of Clairvaux
trans. James Waddell Alexander

Music: Melody by Hans Leo Hassler
arr. Johann Sebastian Bach

PASSION CHORALE 76 76 D

1. O sac-red head, once wound-ed, with grief and pain weighed down, how

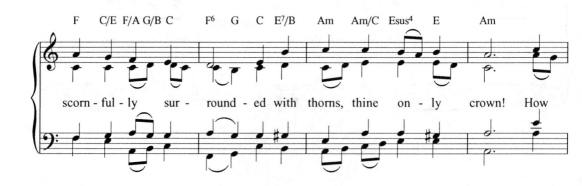

scorn-ful-ly sur-round-ed with thorns, thine on-ly crown! How

pale art thou with an - guish, with sore a-buse and scorn! How

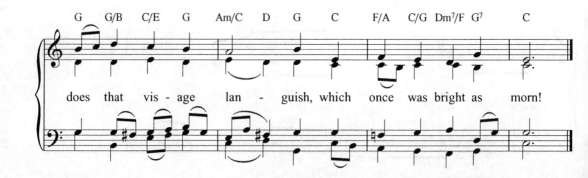

does that vis-age lan - guish, which once was bright as morn!

2. O Lord of life and glory,
   what bliss till now was thine!
   I read the wondrous story,
   I joy to call thee mine.
   Thy grief and thy compassion
   were all for sinners' gain;
   mine, mine was the transgression,
   but thine the deadly pain.

3. What language shall I borrow
   to praise thee, heav'nly friend,
   for this, thy dying sorrow,
   thy pity without end?
   Lord, make me thine for ever,
   nor let me faithless prove;
   O let me never, never
   abuse such dying love!

4. Be near me, Lord, when dying;
   O show thyself to me;
   and for my succour flying,
   come, Lord, to set me free:
   these eyes, new faith receiving,
   from Jesus shall not move;
   for he who dies believing,
   dies safely through thy love.

929 O, the love of God is boundless

Words: D.R. Edwards, revised and adapted
by Graham Kendrick

Music: Graham Kendrick
arr. Richard Lewis

1. O,   the love of God   is bound-less, per - fect, cause - less,

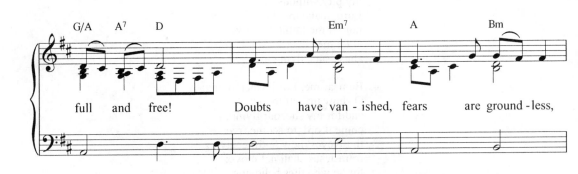

full   and   free!   Doubts   have van - ished, fears   are ground-less,

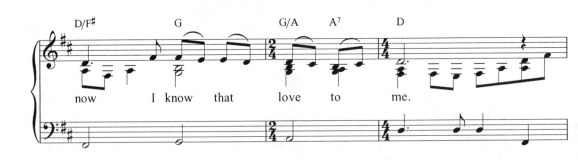

now   I   know   that   love   to   me.

Love,   the source   of   all   my bles - sing, love   that set   it -

self on me. Love, that gave the sin - less vic - tim,

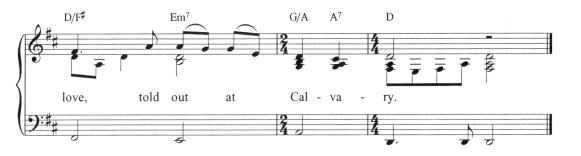

love, told out at Cal - va - ry.

2. O, the cross of Christ is wondrous!
   There I learn God's heart to me
   'midst the silent, deep'ning darkness
   'God is light' I also see.
   Holy claims of justice finding
   full expression in that scene;
   light and love alike are telling
   what his woe and suff'ring means.

3. O, the sight of heav'n is glorious!
   Man in righteousness is there.
   Once the victim, now victorious,
   Jesus lives in glory fair!
   Him, who met the claims of glory
   and the need of ruined man
   on the cross, O wondrous story!
   God has set at his right hand.

4. O, what rest of soul in seeing
   Jesus on his Father's throne!
   Yes, what peace for everflowing
   from God's rest in his own Son!
   Gazing upward into heaven,
   reading glory in his face,
   knowing that 'tis he, once given
   on the cross to take my place.

930 O the passion

Words and Music: Gary Sadler

With a Celtic feel
Verse

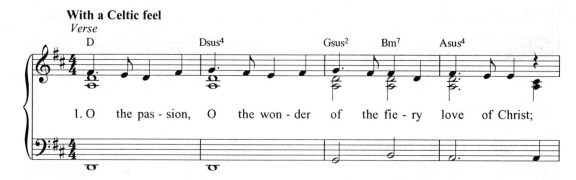

1. O the pas-sion, O the won-der of the fie-ry love of Christ;

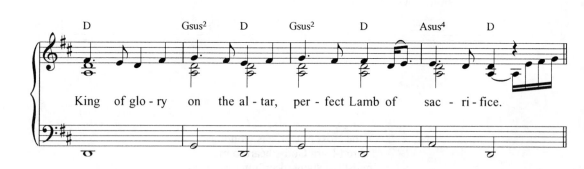

King of glo-ry on the al-tar, per-fect Lamb of sac-ri-fice.

Chorus

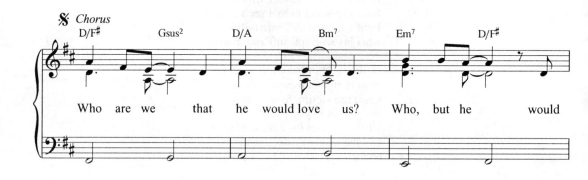

Who are we that he would love us? Who, but he would

give his life? O the pas-sion,

O the won - der of the fie - ry love of Christ.

2. O the wisdom, O the wonder
of the power of the cross;
love so rare no words could tell it,
life himself has died for us.

Who are we that he would save us?
Crucified to give us life;
O the wisdom, O the wonder
of the power of the cross.

3. O the passion, O the wonder
of the fiery love of Christ;
death defeated by his rising,
darkness conquered by his light.

We will sing his praise for ever,
worthy is the Lamb of Life;
O the passion, O the wonder
of the fiery love of Christ.

Who are we that he would love us?
Who, but he would give his life?
O the passion, O the wonder
of the fiery love of Christ.

931 Our Father in heaven   *(The Lord's prayer)*

Words and Music: Brian Doerksen and Michael Hansen

done.   done   on the earth

as it is   in hea - ven.   Let it be done on the earth.   A -

men.   A - men.

932 Our Father, who art in heaven *(The Lord's Prayer)*

Words: Paul Field and Stephen Deal

Music: traditional Scottish melody
adapted by Paul Field and Stephen Deal

933 Our God is great

Words and Music: Dave Bilbrough

Bright and rhythmic

Our God is great. Our God is

great. Our God is great.

Our God is great. Our God is

1. He gave us the wind, the sun and the snow, the

2. The gifts that he brings are new ev'ry day,
from glorious sunset to soft falling rain.
The mist on the hills,
the light and the shade;
come join all creation in praise!

934 Our God is lifted up

Words and Music: Tim Smith

Our God is lift-ed up midst the shouts of joy, our

God is lift-ed up in the sound-ing of the trum-pets; our

God is lift-ed up midst the shouts of joy — shout

joy-ful-ly un-to our God, shout

joy - ful - ly   un - to   our   God.   Our

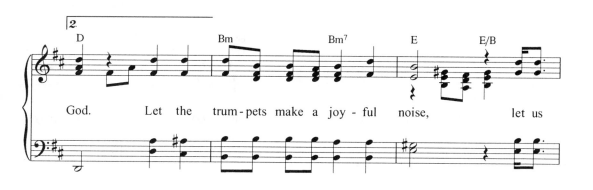

God.   Let   the   trum - pets make a joy - ful   noise,   let us

clap our hands and praise our   God;   for our God is lift - ed up,   our

God is lift - ed up,   our God is lift - ed up   on   high.

935 Our heart

Words and Music: John Chisum and George Searcy

936 Over all the earth

(Lord, reign in me)

Words and Music: Brenton Brown

1. O-ver all the earth, you reign on high, ev-'ry moun-tain stream,

ev-'ry sun-set sky. But my one re-quest, Lord, my on-ly aim

is that you'd reign in me a-gain. Lord, reign in me,

reign in your pow'r o-ver all my dreams, in my dark-est hour.

You are the Lord of all I am, so won't you reign in me a-gain.

2. Over ev'ry thought, over ev'ry word,
   may my life reflect the beauty of my Lord;
   'cause you mean more to me than any earthly thing,
   so won't you reign in me again.

An angel of the Lord appeared to them,
and the glory of the Lord shone around them,
and they were terrified.
But the angel said to them, 'Do not be afraid.
I bring you good news of great joy
that will be for all the people.
Today in the town of David
a Saviour has been born to you;
he is Christ the Lord.
This will be a sign to you:
You will find a baby wrapped in cloths
and lying in a manger.'

Suddenly a great company of the heavenly host
appeared with the angel, praising God and saying,
'Glory to God in the highest,
and on earth peace to all on
whom his favour rests.'

Luke 2:9-14

937 O, your hands of kindness *(Hands of kindness)*

Words and Music: Martin Smith

1. O, your hands of kind-ness are here for me, and I've heard they are silk-en and can car-ry me. How I love you, all I am is you, King of love, I bow.

2. O, your hands of mercy were scarred for me,
   and your body was broken so that I can go free.

3. O, your love that burns me, deeper than the sea,
   and the treasure I find here: the Saviour's love for me.

938 Pour your Holy Spirit upon me   *(Flowing river)*

Words and Music: Rita Baloche

Pour your Ho-ly Spi-rit up-on me,
let your pre-sence fill me up;
make my life a flow-ing ri-ver
of your e-ver-last-ing love.

939 Power and riches belong to you
(You reign)

Words and Music: Richard Lewis

Majestically ($\quarternote$ = 72)

Pow - er and rich - es be - long to you,

my Sa - viour, Re - deem - er and friend.

And all the na - tions be - long to you;

your king - dom, it shall ne - ver end.

Soon all the peo - ples will bow be - fore your throne,

lift - ing prai - ses to your name.

Ev - 'ry knee will bow and ev - 'ry tongue con - fess and pro -

Chorus

claim that you reign. Yes, you

He has taken me to the banquet hall,
and his banner over me is love.

Song of Solomon 2:4

940 Praise him

Words and Music: Clive A. Goodwill
arr. Chris Mitchell

941 Praise him, praise him!

Words: Frances Jane van Alstyne (Fanny J. Crosby)

Music: Chester G. Allen

PRAISE HIM 12 10 12 10 11 10 12 10

1. Praise him, praise him! Je - sus, our bles - sed Re - deem - er!
Sing, O earth, his won - der - ful love pro - claim!
Hail him, hail him! High - est arch - an - gels in glo - ry;
strength and hon - our give to his ho - ly name!
Like a shep - herd, Je - sus will guard his child - ren,

in his arms he car-ries them all day long.

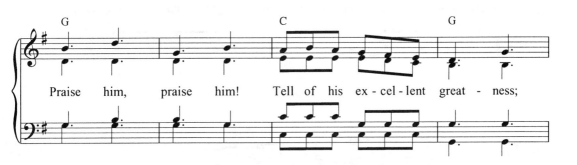

Praise him, praise him! Tell of his ex-cel-lent great-ness;

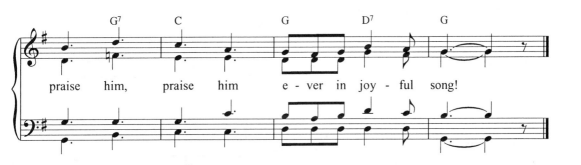

praise him, praise him e-ver in joy-ful song!

2. Praise him, praise him! Jesus, our blessèd Redeemer!
For our sins he suffered, and bled, and died!
He — our rock, our hope of eternal salvation,
hail him, hail him! Jesus the crucified!
Sound his praises — Jesus who bore our sorrows,
love unbounded, wonderful, deep and strong.

3. Praise him, praise him! Jesus, our blessèd Redeemer!
Heav'nly portals, loud with hosannas ring!
Jesus, Saviour, reigneth for ever and ever:
crown him, crown him! Prophet, and Priest, and King!
Christ is coming, over the world victorious,
pow'r and glory unto the Lord belong.

942 Praise him, you heavens

(Great in power)

Words and Music: Russell Fragar

Praise him, you hea - vens and all that's a - bove.
Praise him, the sun, moon and bright shi - ning stars.

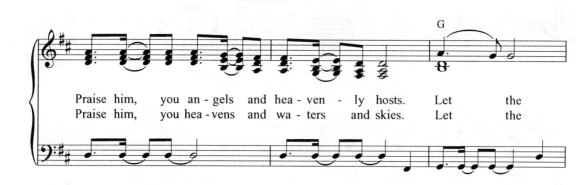

Praise him, you an - gels and hea - ven - ly hosts. Let the
Praise him, you hea - vens and wa - ters and skies. Let the

whole earth praise him.
whole earth praise him.

Chorus

Great in pow - er, great in

Sovereign Lord,
you have made the heavens and the earth
by your great power and outstretched arm.
Nothing is too hard for you.
O great and powerful God,
whose name is the Lord Almighty,
great are your purposes and mighty are your deeds.

Jeremiah 32:17, 18b, 19a

943 Praise the Lord

Words and Music: Bryn Haworth

him,   our   times   are   in   his

hands.   My

heart will al - ways   trust   him,   he's the Rock

on which I stand.   Praise   the Lord,

2. O what a friend is Jesus,
   his love will never end.
   Cast all your cares upon him,
   he's our refuge and our strength.
   He heals the broken-hearted
   and sets the captives free;
   place no one else above him,
   all the earth will one day sing.

944 Praise the Lord

Words and Music: Tim Lomax
arr. Dave Bankhead

2. Praise him, sun, praise him, moon.
   Praise him, all you bright stars,
   praise him, all you highest heav'ns.
   All you deepest oceans,
   come and praise the Lord.

945 Praise to the Lord, the Almighty

Words: Joachim Neander
trans. Catherine Winkworth

Music: from *Praxis Pietatis Melica*

LOBE DEN HERREN 14 14 4 7 8

2. Praise to the Lord, who o'er all things so wondrously reigneth,
   shieldeth thee gently from harm, or when fainting sustaineth:
   hast thou not seen
   how thy heart's wishes have been
   granted in what he ordaineth?

3. Praise to the Lord, who doth prosper thy work and defend thee,
   surely his goodness and mercy shall daily attend thee:
   ponder anew
   what the Almighty can do,
   if to the end he befriend thee.

4. Praise to the Lord, O let all that is in us adore him!
   All that hath life and breath, come now with praises before him.
   Let the 'Amen'
   sound from his people again,
   gladly for ay we adore him.

946 Put on the garments of praise *(Garments of praise)*

Words and Music: Jamie Harvill
arr. Chris Mitchell

(Hal - le -)

lu – jah, sing hal-le - lu – jah, we give all hon-our and praise to your

name. Hal - le - lu – jah, sing hal - le - lu – jah, we trade our

sor - rows   for gar - ments of praise.   Hal - le - praise.

947 Rain down

Words and Music: Richard Lewis

Rain down, Ho-ly Spi-rit, rain down on

this thirs-ty land. We need your love, we need your pow'r, we

need a touch from your hand this hour. We cry for more of you,

Ho-ly Spi-rit, rain down.

Fa - ther, send the rain. Pour

For your glo - ry and your hon-

- our, for your glo - ry,

Ho - ly Spi - rit, rain down.

948 Rejoice, the Lord is King!

Words: Charles Wesley

Music: George Frideric Handel

GOPSAL 66 66 and Refrain

1. Re-joice, the Lord is King! Your Lord and King a-dore; mor-tals give thanks and sing, and tri-umph e-ver-more. Lift up your heart, lift up your voice; re-joice, a-gain I say, re-joice.

2. Jesus the Saviour reigns,
   the God of truth and love;
   when he had purged our stains,
   he took his seat above.

3. His kingdom cannot fail;
   he rules o'er earth and heav'n;
   the keys of death and hell
   are to our Jesus giv'n.

4. He sits at God's right hand
   till all his foes submit,
   and bow to his command,
   and fall beneath his feet.

949 Right now

Words and Music: Nick Coetzee

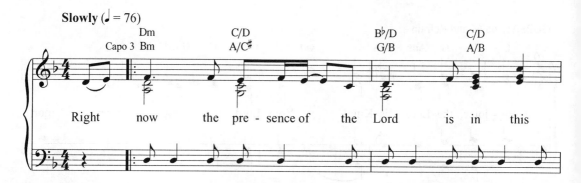

They will be called oaks of righteousness,
a planting of the Lord
for the display of his splendour.

Isaiah 61:3b

950 Rock of ages

Words: Augustus Montague Toplady, alt.

Music: Thomas Hastings

TOPLADY 77 77 77

1. Rock of a-ges, cleft for me, let me hide my-self in thee; let the water and the blood, from thy ri-ven side which flowed, be of sin the dou-ble cure: cleanse me from its guilt and pow'r.

2. Not the labours of my hands
   can fulfil thy law's demands;
   could my zeal no respite know,
   could my tears for ever flow,
   all for sin could not atone:
   thou must save, and thou alone.

3. Nothing in my hands I bring,
   simply to thy cross I cling;
   naked, come to thee for dress;
   helpless, look to thee for grace;
   tainted, to the fountain fly;
   wash me, Saviour, or I die.

4. While I draw this fleeting breath,
   when mine eyelids close in death,
   when I soar through tracts unknown,
   see thee on thy judgement throne;
   Rock of ages, cleft for me,
   let me hide myself in thee.

951 Rock of ages

Words: Augustus Montague Toplady
revised and adapted by Graham Kendrick

Music: Graham Kendrick
arr. Richard Lewis

1.Rock of a - ges, cleft for me, let me hide my - self in thee. Let the wa - ter and the blood from your wound-ed side which flowed be of sin the dou - ble cure, cleanse me from its guilt and pow'r. My

Last time to Coda

Chorus

Rock (my Rock), my Je - sus, my Rock. My Rock (my

CODA

Rock), my Je - sus, my Rock. 2. Not the thee. My
3. No - thing
4. While I

Rock (my Rock), my Je - sus, my Rock. My

Rock (my Rock), my Je - sus, my Rock. My Rock.

2. Not the labours of my hands
   can fulfil your law's demands.
   Could my zeal no respite know,
   could my tears for ever flow,
   all for sin could not atone,
   you must save and you alone.

3. Nothing in my hand I bring,
   simply to your cross I cling.
   Naked, come to you for dress,
   helpless, look to you for grace.
   Foul, I to the fountain fly,
   wash me, Saviour, or I die.

4. While I draw this fleeting breath,
   when my eyelids close in death,
   when I soar to worlds unknown,
   see you on your judgement throne,
   Rock of ages, cleft for me,
   let me hide myself in thee.

952 Saviour, like a shepherd lead us

Words: *Hymns for the Young* (1836)
attributed to Dorothy A. Thrupp

Music: William B. Bradbury
arr. Chris Mitchell

1. Sav - iour, like a shep-herd lead us, much we need thy ten-der

care; in thy plea-sant pas-tures feed us,

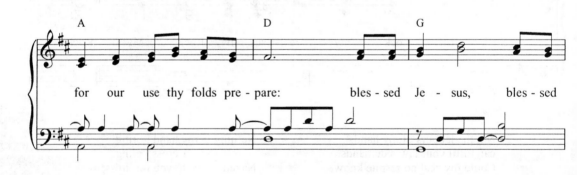

for our use thy folds pre-pare: bles-sed Je - sus, bles-sed

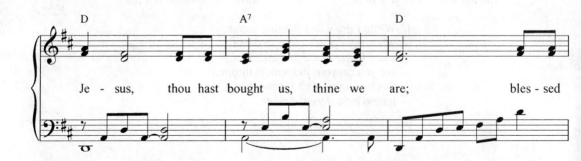

Je - sus, thou hast bought us, thine we are; bles-sed

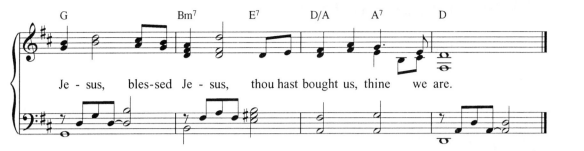

Je - sus, bles-sed Je - sus, thou hast bought us, thine we are.

2. We are thine, do thou befriend us,
   be the guardian of our way;
   keep thy flock, from sin defend us,
   seek us when we go astray:
   blessèd Jesus, blessèd Jesus,
   hear, O hear us when we pray;
   blessèd Jesus, blessèd Jesus,
   hear, O hear us when we pray.

3. Thou hast promised to receive us,
   poor and sinful though we be;
   thou hast mercy to relieve us,
   grace to cleanse and pow'r to free:
   blessèd Jesus, blessèd Jesus,
   early let us turn to thee;
   blessèd Jesus, blessèd Jesus,
   early let us turn to thee.

4. Early let us seek thy favour;
   early let us do thy will;
   blessèd Lord and only Saviour,
   with thy love our beings fill:
   blessèd Jesus, blessèd Jesus,
   thou hast loved us, love us still;
   blessèd Jesus, blessèd Jesus,
   thou hast loved us, love us still.

953 Say the name of love

Words and Music: Graham Kendrick
arr. Richard Lewis

954 Say the word   *(I simply live for you)*

Words and Music: Russell Fragar
arr. Chris Mitchell

by your word, you set the cap - tives free. There is

no - thing in this world that you can - not do. I sim - ply live,

I sim - ply live for you. Say the

955 Search me, O God

Words and Music: Ian Mizen and Andy Pressdee
arr. Chris Mitchell

Search me, O God, and know my heart, lead me in your ways for e-ver. I want to be holy, giv-ing ev-'ry-thing to you. I want to be pure in heart and pure in mind. I want to be holy,

al - ways pleas - ing you, I want to live for you.

956 See, amid the winter's snow

Words: Edward Caswall

Music: John Goss

HUMILITY (OXFORD) 77 77 and Refrain

1. See, a-mid the win-ter's snow, born for us on earth be-low,

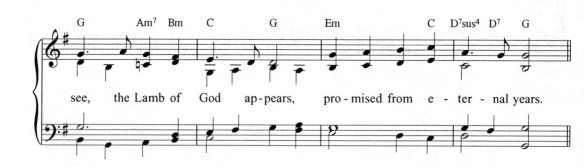

see, the Lamb of God ap-pears, pro-mised from e-ter-nal years.

Hail, thou e-ver-bles-sed morn! Hail, re-demp-tion's hap-py dawn!

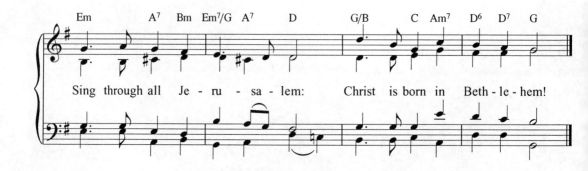

Sing through all Je-ru-sa-lem: Christ is born in Beth-le-hem!

2. Lo, within a manger lies
   he who built the starry skies,
   he who, throned in heights sublime,
   sits amid the cherubim.

3. Say, ye holy shepherds, say,
   what your joyful news today;
   wherefore have you left your sheep
   on the lonely mountain steep?

4. 'As we watched at dead of night,
   lo, we saw a wondrous light;
   angels, singing peace on earth,
   told us of the Saviour's birth.'

5. Sacred infant, all divine,
   what a tender love was thine,
   thus to come from highest bliss,
   down to such a world as this!

6. Teach, O teach us, holy child,
   by thy face so meek and mild,
   teach us to resemble thee
   in thy sweet humility.

957 Send us the rain, Lord

Words and Music: Dave Wellington

1. Send us the rain, Lord, rain of your Spi - rit, rain on this

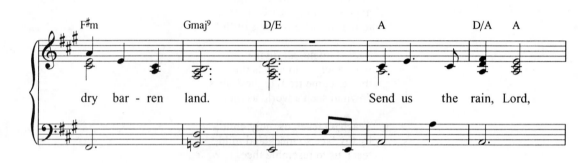

dry bar - ren land. Send us the rain, Lord,

rain to re - vive us; cleanse us and fill us a - gain.

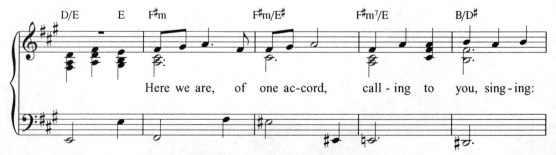

Here we are, of one ac-cord, call - ing to you, sing - ing:

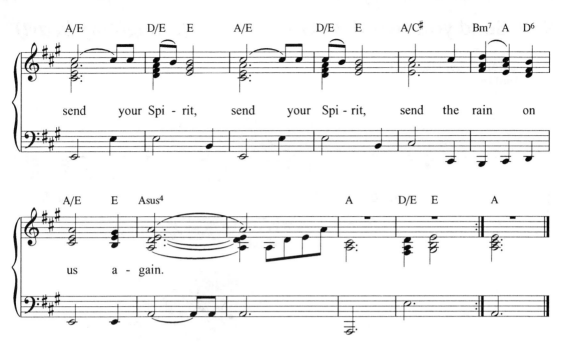

send your Spi - rit, send your Spi - rit, send the rain on us a - gain.

2. Pour out your wine, Lord,
   wine of your Spirit,
   wine that would teach us to love.
   Pour out your wine, Lord,
   oh, how we need you
   to quench the thirst of our hearts.
   Here we are of one accord,
   calling to you, singing:
   send your Spirit,
   send your Spirit,
   pour your wine on us again.

3. Breathe now upon us,
   breath of your Spirit,
   breath to bring life to these bones.
   Breathe now upon us
   life of abundance,
   holiness, wisdom, love, truth.
   Here we are of one accord,
   calling to you, singing:
   send your Spirit,
   send your Spirit,
   breathe your life on us again.

4. Send down the fire,
   fire of your Spirit,
   Refiner's fire to fulfil.
   Send down the fire,
   fire to consume us,
   reveal your power once more.
   Here we are of one accord,
   calling to you, singing:
   send your Spirit,
   send your Spirit,
   send the fire on us again.

958 Send your word, O God

(Plough my heart)

Words and Music: Paul Banderet
arr. Richard Lewis

Send your word, O God, that cuts to the heart of me. Plant your word, O God, that be-comes a part of me. Re-veal your vis- ion of what you want of me, O make me rea - dy for your com-ing, Lord.

959 Shackled by a heavy burden

(He touched me)

Words and Music: William J. Gaither
arr. Richard Lewis

1. Shack-led by a hea-vy bur-den, 'neath a load of

guilt and shame; then the hand of Je - sus

touched me, and now I am no lon-ger the same. He

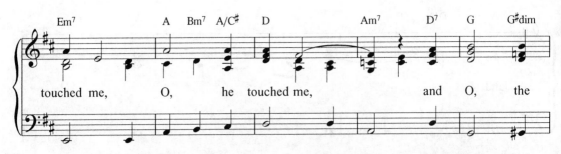

touched me, O, he touched me, and O, the

joy that floods my soul! Some-thing hap-pened, and

now I know, he touched me and made me whole.

2. Since I met this blessèd Saviour,
   since he cleansed and made me whole;
   I will never cease to praise him,
   I'll shout it while eternity rolls.

960 Should he who made the stars

(We sing your mercies)

Words and Music: Mark Altrogge

1. Should he who made the stars be hung up-on a tree? And should the hands that healed be dri-ven through for me? Should he who gave us bread be made to swal-low gall? Should he who gave us breath and life be slaugh-tered for us all?

2. Should he who is the light be cast into the dark?
   And should the Lord of love be pierced through his own heart?
   Should he who called us friends be deserted by us all?
   Should he who lived a sinless life be punished for our fall?

961 Sing a song for the nations

Words and Music: Andy Smith

1. Sing a song for the na- tions, sing a song for the earth;
2. Sing a song from your heart now, sing a song with your life.

God's cho- sen peo- ple to shine out his
You are a ves- sel for the glo- ry of

worth. Bro- thers and sis- ters with har- mo- nies
Christ. Sing to the bro- ken: 'Your heal- er has

rare. Beau- ti- ful mu- sic is fill- ing the air.
come. You can find rest in the arms of the Son'.

Chorus

Let our songs ring out all o- ver the earth.

962 Sing to the Lord

(Awaken the dawn)

Words and Music: Stuart Garrard

With a lilt

1. Sing to the Lord with all of your heart; sing of the glo - ry that's

due to his name. Sing to the Lord with all of your soul,

join all of hea - ven and earth to pro - claim: You are the Lord, the

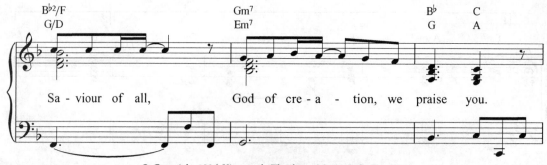

Sa - viour of all, God of cre - a - tion, we praise you.

We sing the songs that a-wak-en the dawn, God of cre-a - tion, we praise you.

Last time

2. Sing to the Lord with all of your mind,
with understanding give thanks to the King.
Sing to the Lord with all of your strength,
living our lives as a praise offering.

963 Sing unto the Lord

Words and Music: Leon Patillo

1. Sing un-to the Lord a new song, let his prai-ses fill the
2. Sing un-to the Lord a new song, for he loves to hear our

tem-ple. He is the King of kings and the Lord of lords.
prai-ses. Let all of cre-a-tion sing, 'Glo-ry to our God!'

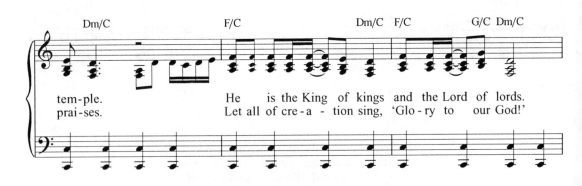

Bow down be-fore him.
Bow down be- -fore him.

Hal-le-lu-jah! Glo-ry to

964 Son of Man

Words and Music: David Bird, Richard Lacy and Sarah Lacy
arr. Chris Mitchell

Son of Man, led to die on a cross, nailed and bleed-ing, and the
life ebbed a-way, though my sins were red as scar-let, your

hea-vens dark-ened in your name. There was dust, there was heat, there was
blood has washed them white as snow, and a death bring-ing life, though be-

pain and there was glo-ry and ful-fil-ment of the pro-phet's words. Son of
yond my un-der-stand-ing, is made real in me if I be-lieve.

Man, you shed your blood, I could know no great-er

1. C/E   F   Gsus⁴   G

love.

2. C/E   F   Gsus⁴   G   Gsus⁴

As   your   love.   O-pen   hearts   will   re - ceive   all   the

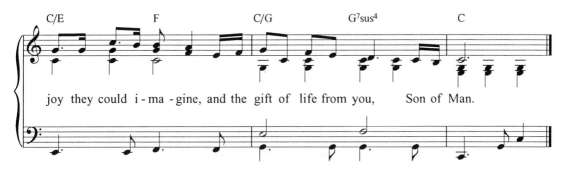

C/E   F   C/G   G⁷sus⁴   C

joy   they   could   i - ma - gine,   and   the   gift   of   life   from   you,   Son   of   Man.

To him who loves us
and has freed us from our sins by his blood,
and has made us to be a kingdom and priests
to serve his God and Father –
to him be glory and power for ever and ever!
Amen.

Revelation 1:5b-6

965 Spirit, how we hunger for your presence
(Feast at your table)

Words and Music: Steve and Vikki Cook

1. Spi - rit, how we hun - ger for your pre - sence,
2. Fa - ther, you've pre - pared for us a ban - quet,

with no - thing else will we be sat - is -
in hon - our of the vict - 'ry of your

fied.
Son.

How we long to taste your la - vish
For he se - cured the way for our com -

good - ness,
mun - ion,

and fill our souls with hea -
that we could know the ful -

- ven's bread of life.
- ness of your love.

And so we come to you

966 Spirit of the living God *(Flow like a river)*

Words and Music: Billy Funk
arr. Chris Mitchell

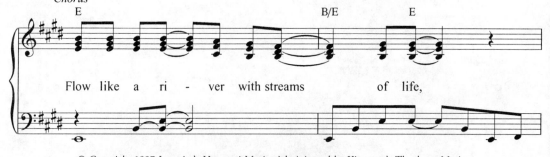

flow like a ri - ver, flow free;

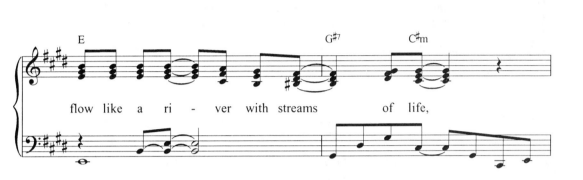

flow like a ri - ver with streams of life,

sett - ing your peo - ple free.

967 Standing in your presence *(I live to know you)*

Words and Music: Darlene Zschech

1. Standing in your presence, Lord, my heart and life are changed;
just to love you and to live to see your beauty and your grace.

called me, I will follow your will for me I'm sure.
Let your heart beat be my heart's cry, let me live to serve your call.

Chorus
Heaven and earth cry out your name, nations rise up and see your face; and your kingdom is established as I live to know you more.

968 Sunrise awakening

(Day of the Dance)

Words and Music: Andy Smith and Johnny Markin

1. Sun-rise a-wa-ken-ing joy to our lips; dawn is bring-ing re-vi-val. Hea-ven is sound-ing a glo-ri-ous beat; saints come a-live to its rhy-thm. Ris-ing, turn-ing hearts to the call of the Sa-viour. Break-ing, burn-ing chains that have kept us from

2. See, now, the lame as they rise to their feet;
   hear, now, the mute tongue is singing.
   Hearts that were barren in winter's decay
   spring forth in joyous abandon.

969 Teach me thy way, O Lord

Words: B. Mansell Ramsey

Music: B. Mansell Ramsey arr. Beryl Croft

THE PATH DIVINE 64 64 66 64

1. Teach me thy way, O Lord, teach me thy way!
Thy gra - cious aid af - ford, teach me thy way!
Help me to walk a - right, more by faith, less by sight;
lead me with heav'n - ly light: teach me thy way.

2. When doubts and fears arise,
teach me thy way!
When storms o'erspread the skies,
teach me thy way!
Shine through the cloud and rain,
through sorrow, toil, and pain;
make thou my pathway plain:
teach me thy way!

3. Long as my life shall last,
teach me thy way!
Where'er my lot be cast,
teach me thy way!
Until the race is run,
until the journey's done,
until the crown is won,
teach me thy way!

970 Thank you for your mighty power *(So good to me)*

Words and Music: C. Mundy, L. Petersen and J. Price
arr. Chris Mitchell

1. Thank you for your migh - ty pow - er that you showed on Cal - va - ry. Lord, I'm here to - day, prais - ing your name 'cause you set me free.

2. Thank you for life in the Spi - rit that gives me li - ber - ty, all my days are filled with vic - to - ry 'cause you set me free.

Free from sin, free from shame,
Free to dance, free to sing,

So good, so good to me.

So good, so good to me.

D.S.

CODA

Lord, you've been so good, Lord,

you've been so good, Lord, you've been so good to me.

Great and marvellous are your deeds,
Lord God Almighty.
Just and true are your ways,
King of the ages.
Who will not fear you, O Lord,
and bring glory to your name?
For you alone are holy.
All nations will come
and worship before you,
for your righteous acts have been revealed.

Revelation 15:3-4

971 The angels around your throne

Words and Music: Richard lewis

2. The angels around your throne,
they cry 'Worthy is the Lamb.' *etc.*

972 The blood that Jesus shed for me
(The blood will never lose its power)

Words and Music: Andraé Crouch
arr. Richard Lewis

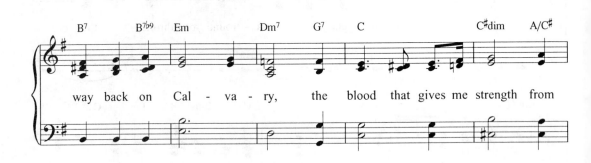

val - ley. The blood that gives me strength from day to day, it will ne - ver lose its pow'r! 2. It

2. It soothes my doubt and calms my fears,
   and it dries all my tears;
   the blood that gives me strength from day to day,
   it will never lose its pow'r.

973 The darkest hour, Lord Jesus

Words: G.R. Cowell
adapted Graham Kendrick

Music: Melody by Hans Leo Hassler (1564-1612)
harm. Johann Sebastian Bach (1685-1750)

PASSION CHORALE 76 76 D

1. The darkest hour, Lord Jesus, that rolled o'er your blest head called forth the sweetest fragrance that e'er on earth was shed. That cup so full, so bitter — the wormwood and the gall — directly from your Father you did accept it all.

2. What perfect, meek submission! Your will, not mine be done.
   Obedience full, unquestioned; perfection of a Son!
   Thus prostrate there before him, your sweat as drops of blood
   and so to be the victim, the spotless Lamb of God!

3. Yet you, O holy suff'rer, could 'Abba, Father!' cry
   through all your woe abiding in sonship's perfect tie.
   Through suffering made perfect in heav'n our leader now;
   captain of our salvation! With rev'rent hearts we bow.

4. By this you have, Lord Jesus, our hearts' affection gained.
   How can we give you comfort for what you have sustained?
   Entire and full devotion alone can worthy be
   till, love to love responsive, your glorious face we see.

974 The first Nowell

Words: from William Sandys'
Christmas Carols, Ancient and Modern, alt.

Music: traditional English melody
arr. John Stainer

THE FIRST NOWELL Irregular and Refrain

1. The first No-well the an-gel did say was to cer-tain poor

shep-herds in fields as they lay: in fields where they lay

keep-ing their sheep, on a cold win-ter's night that was so deep.

Chorus

No - well,   No - well,   No - well,   No - well,

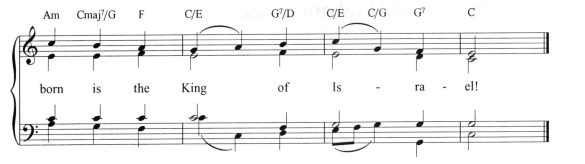

born is the King of Is - ra - el!

2. They lookèd up and saw a star,
   shining in the east, beyond them far,
   and to the earth it gave great light,
   and so it continued both day and night.

3. And by the light of that same star,
   three wise men came from country far;
   to seek for a king was their intent,
   and to follow the star wherever it went.

4. This star drew nigh to the north-west,
   o'er Bethlehem it took its rest,
   and there it did both stop and stay
   right over the place where Jesus lay.

5. Then entered in those wise men three,
   full rev'rently upon their knee,
   and offered there in his presence,
   their gold and myrrh and frankincense.

6. Then let us all with one accord
   sing praises to our heav'nly Lord,
   who with the Father we adore
   and Spirit blest for evermore.

975 The God of Abraham praise

Words: Thomas Olivers
based on the Hebrew *Yigdal*, alt.

Music: traditional Hebrew melody

LEONI 66 84 D

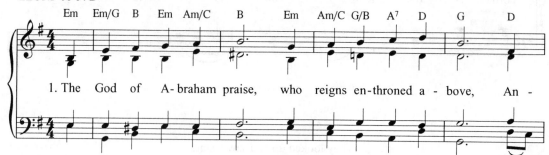

1. The God of A-braham praise, who reigns en-throned a - bove, An -

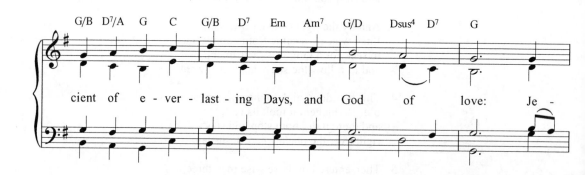

cient of e - ver - last - ing Days, and God of love: Je -

ho - vah, great 'I Am', by earth and heav'n con - fessed; we

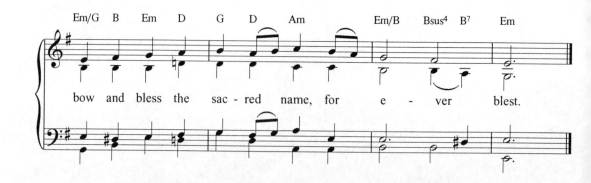

bow and bless the sac - red name, for e - ver blest.

2. The God of Abraham praise,
   at whose supreme command
   from earth we rise, and seek the joys
   at his right hand:
   we all on earth forsake,
   its wisdom, fame and pow'r,
   and him our only portion make,
   our shield and tow'r.

3. He by himself has sworn —
   we on his oath depend —
   we shall, on eagles' wings upborne,
   to heav'n ascend:
   we shall behold his face,
   we shall his pow'r adore,
   and sing the wonders of his grace
   for evermore.

4. There dwells the Lord our King,
   the Lord our righteousness,
   triumphant o'er the world and sin,
   the Prince of Peace,
   on Zion's sacred height
   his Kingdom still maintains,
   and glorious with his saints in light
   for ever reigns.

5. The whole triumphant host
   give thanks to God on high:
   'Hail, Father, Son and Holy Ghost!'
   they ever cry:
   Hail, Abraham's God and ours!
   We join the heav'nly throng,
   and celebrate with all our pow'rs
   in endless song.

In a loud voice they sang:
'Worthy is the Lamb, who was slain,
to receive power and wealth and
wisdom and strength
and honour and glory and praise!'

Revelation 5:12

976 The grace

Words and Musc: Tim Lomax

977 The greatest thing in all my life

Words and Music: Mark Pendergrass
arr. Chris Mitchell

great-est thing   in   all my life   is   know - ing   you.

2. The greatest thing in all my life is loving you;
   the greatest thing in all my life is loving you.
   I want to love you more, I want to love you more.
   The greatest thing in all my life is loving you.

3. The greatest thing in all my life is serving you;
   the greatest thing in all my life is serving you.
   I want to serve you more, I want to serve you more.
   The greatest thing in all my life is serving you.

978 The great God of heaven

Words: H.R. Bramley

Music: traditional English carol

A VIRGIN UNSPOTTED 11 11 11 11 and Refrain

1. The great God of heaven is come down to earth, his
mo - ther a vir - gin, and sin - less his birth; the
Fa - ther e - ter - nal his Fa - ther a - lone: he
sleeps in the man - ger; he reigns on the throne:

Chorus

then let us a - dore him, and praise his great love: to

save us poor sin - ners he came from a - bove.

2. A babe on the breast of a maiden he lies,
   yet sits with the Father on high in the skies;
   before him their faces the seraphim hide,
   while Joseph stands waiting, unscared, by his side:

3. Lo! here is Emmanuel, here is the Child,
   the Son that was promised to Mary so mild;
   whose pow'r and dominion shall ever increase,
   the Prince that shall rule o'er a kingdom of peace:

4. The Wonderful Counsellor, boundless in might,
   the Father's own image, the beam of his light;
   behold him now wearing the likeness of man,
   weak, helpless, and speechless, in measure a span:

5. O wonder of wonders, which none can unfold:
   the Ancient of Days is an hour or two old;
   the maker of all things is made of the earth,
   man is worshipped by angels, and God comes to birth:

6. The word in the bliss of the Godhead remains,
   yet in flesh comes to suffer the keenest of pains;
   he is that he was, and for ever shall be,
   but becomes that he was not, for you and for me.

979 The head that once was crowned with thorns

Words: Thomas Kelly

Music: Jeremiah Clarke

ST MAGNUS CM

1. The head that once was crowned with thorns is crowned with glo - ry now: a roy - al di - a - dem a - dorns the migh - ty vic - tor's brow.

2. The highest place that heav'n affords
is his, is his by right.
The King of kings and Lord of lords,
and heav'n's eternal light.

3. The joy of all who dwell above,
the joy of all below,
to whom he manifests his love,
and grants his name to know.

4. To them the cross, with all its shame,
with all its grace is giv'n;
their name an everlasting name,
their joy the joy of heav'n.

5. They suffer with their Lord below,
they reign with him above,
their profit and their joy to know
the myst'ry of his love.

6. The cross he bore is life and health,
though shame and death to him;
his people's hope, his people's wealth,
their everlasting theme.

980 The heavens are open

Words and Music: Jo Puleston
arr. Dave Bankhead

The hea-vens are o - pen now, the hea-vens are o - pen now,

the hea-vens are o - pen now; the pre-sence of God

is here. The hea-vens are o - pen now,

*(I know the) the hea-vens are o - pen now, (I see the)

hea-vens are o - pen now; the pre-sence of God is here.

Echos are optional

He said, 'If you listen carefully
to the voice of the Lord your God
and do what is right in his eyes,
if you pay attention to his commands
and keep all his decrees,
I will not bring on you any of the diseases
I brought on the Egyptians,
for I am the Lord, who heals you.'

Exodus 15:26

981 The heavens, they preach

Words and Music: Lex Loizides

1. The hea - vens, they preach, they preach, they preach the
   pro - phets, they preached, they preached, they preached that
   peo - ple will preach, we'll preach, we'll preach the

glo - ri - ous splen-dour of God. The stars in the sky seem
one day a Sa - viour would come; and sud-den - ly men heard a
un - fail - ing ri - ches of Christ, there's no one who's fal - len too

so out of reach, yet they whis - per his won-der - ful love.
hea - ven - ly speech, the voice of God's on - ly Son.
far from his reach, who can't come from death in - to life.

Day af - ter day in a ser - mon of na - ture the works of his hands lift their
Day af - ter day in the streets and the tem - ple he taught them and met their needs,
Day af - ter day at the dawn of re - vi - val the mul - ti - tudes seek his face,

982 The Holy Spirit is here   *(Church on fire)*

Words and Music: Russell Fragar

Fast Rock 'n' Roll

1. The Ho-ly Spi-rit is here, and his pow-er is real. A-ny-thing can hap-pen, and it pro-ba-bly will. Some-thing ve-ry good, some-thing good is go-ing on a-round here.

light that shines to make the dark-ness dis-ap-pear, there's a po-wer at work, but there's no-thing to fear.

2. Well, there's a

Chorus

This is a church on fire, this is the Ho-ly Spi-rit flame.

983 The King of love

(The King has come)

Words and Music: Stuart Townend and Kevin Jamieson

2. My Lover's breath is sweetest wine,
   I am his prize, and he is mine;
   how can a sinner know such joy:
   because of Jesus.
   The wounds of love are in his hands,
   the price is paid for sinful man;
   accepted child, forgiven son:
   because of Jesus.

Now the Lord is the Spirit,
and where the Spirit of the Lord is, there is freedom.
And we, who with unveiled faces all reflect the Lord's glory,
are being transformed into his likeness with ever-increasing glory,
which comes from the Lord, who is the Spirit.

2 Corinthians 3:17-18

984 The King of love my shepherd is

Words: Henry Williams Baker
based on Psalm 23

Music: traditional Irish melody

ST COLUMBA 87 87

1. The King of love my shepherd is, whose good-ness fail-eth ne-ver; I no-thing lack if I am his and he is mine for e-ver.

2. Where streams of living water flow
my ransomed soul he leadeth,
and where the verdant pastures grow
with food celestial feedeth.

3. Perverse and foolish oft I strayed,
but yet in love he sought me,
and on his shoulder gently laid,
and home, rejoicing, brought me.

4. In death's dark vale I fear no ill
with thee, dear Lord, beside me;
thy rod and staff my comfort still,
thy cross before to guide me.

5. Thou spread'st a table in my sight,
thy unction grace bestoweth:
and O what transport of delight
from thy pure chalice floweth!

6. And so through all the length of days
thy goodness faileth never;
good Shepherd, may I sing thy praise
within thy house for ever.

985 The Lord is gracious and compassionate

Words and Music: Graham Ord

The Lord is gra - cious and com - pas - sion-ate,

slow to an - ger and rich in love.

The Lord is gra - cious and com - pas -sion-ate,

To continue

Last time

Fine

slow to an - ger and rich in love. rich in love.

The Lord is good to all, he has com - pas-sion on all that he has made.

986 The Lord is marching out

Words and Music: Richard Lewis

987 The Lord is present here

Words and Music: Graham Kendrick
arr. Richard Lewis

join - ing with all hea-ven to ac - claim: Ho - ly, ho - ly, ho - ly Lord,

God of pow'r and might, heav'n and earth are full of your

glo - ry. Ho - ly, ho - ly, ho - ly Lord, God of pow'r and might, heav'n and

earth are full of your glo - ry. 3. Let glo - ry.

988 The Lord's my shepherd

Words and Music: Stuart Townend
based on Psalm 23

2. He guides my ways in righteousness,
   and he anoints my head with oil;
   and my cup — it overflows with joy,
   I feast on his pure delights.

3. And though I walk the darkest path —
   I will not fear the evil one,
   for you are with me, and your rod and staff
   are the comfort I need to know.

989 There is a fountain filled with blood

Words: William Cowper

Music: traditional melody

THERE IS A FOUNTAIN CM and Refrain

1. There is a fountain filled with blood, drawn from Immanuel's veins, and sinners plunged beneath that flood lose all their guilty stains.

Chorus

Lose all their guilty stains, lose all their guilty stains; and
Wash all my sins away, wash all my sins away; and

sinners plunged beneath that flood lose all their guilty stains.
there may I, though vile as he, wash all my sins away.

2. The dying thief rejoiced to see
   that fountain in his day;
   and there may I, though vile as he,
   wash all my sins away.

3. I do believe, I will believe,
   that Jesus died for me!
   That on the cross he shed his blood,
   from sin to set me free.

4. Dear dying Lamb! Thy precious blood
   shall never lose its pow'r,
   till all the ransomed church of God
   be saved to sin no more.

5. E'er since by faith I saw the stream
   thy flowing wounds supply,
   redeeming love has been my theme,
   and shall be till I die.

Trust in the Lord with all your heart
and lean not on your own understanding.

Proverbs 3:5

990 There is a green hill far away

Music: Cecil Frances Alexander

Music: William Horsley

HORSLEY CM

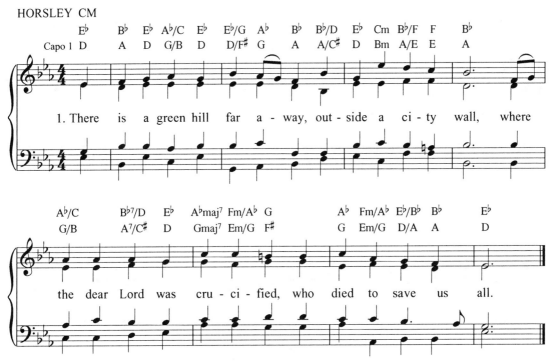

2. We may not know, we cannot tell,
   what pains he had to bear,
   but we believe it was for us
   he hung and suffered there.

3. He died that we might be forgiv'n,
   he died to make us good;
   that we might go at last to heav'n,
   saved by his precious blood.

4. There was no other good enough
   to pay the price of sin;
   he only could unlock the gate
   of heav'n, and let us in.

5. O, dearly, dearly has he loved,
   and we must love him too,
   and trust in his redeeming blood,
   and try his works to do.

991 There is a name I love to hear

Words: F. Whitfield

Music: W.M. Rudd

1. There is a name I love to hear, I love to

speak its worth; it sounds like mu - sic

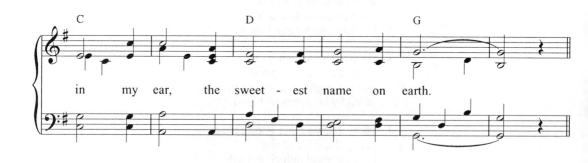

in my ear, the sweet - est name on earth.

Chorus

Voice 1:
O how I love the Sa - viour's name, O how I

Voice 2:
How I love the Sa - viour's name, how I

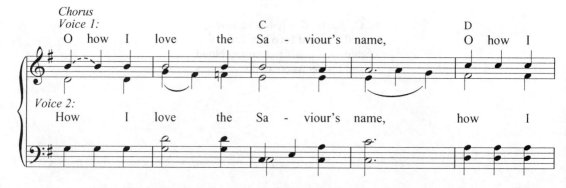

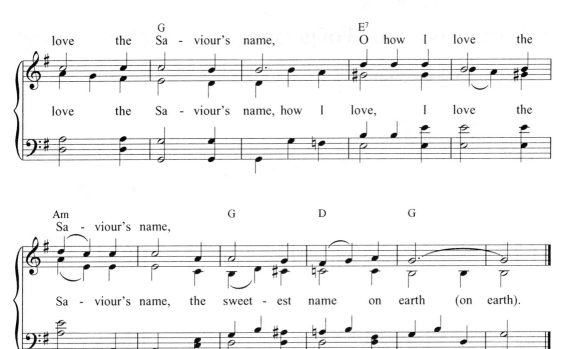

love the Saviour's name, O how I love the
love the Saviour's name, how I love, I love the
Saviour's name, Saviour's name, the sweet-est name on earth (on earth).

2. It tells me of a Saviour's love,
   who died to set me free;
   it tells me of his precious blood,
   the sinner's perfect plea.

3. It tells of one whose loving heart
   can feel my deepest woe;
   who in my sorrow bears a part
   that none can bear below.

4. It bids my trembling heart rejoice,
   it dries each rising tear;
   it tells me in a still, small voice,
   to trust and never fear.

992 There is a sound of great rejoicing *(Make a way)*

Words and Music: Michael Battersby

Not to us, Lord, not to us
but to your name be the glory,
because of your love and faithfulness.

Psalm 115:1

993 There is freedom at the cross
(You bought me freedom)

Words and Music: David Jones

1. There is free-dom at the cross, end-less hope for all of us,
2. There is mer-cy at the cross, we were bro-ken, dead and lost

the price was paid now we can all go free.
but you've res-cued me, I've been re-deemed.

No great-er love was e - ver shown, you were bro-ken, I am whole.
I did not de-serve this grace, out of love you free - ly gave

I can't be-lieve what you have done for me.
life to ran-som me, now I'm saved.

King of hea-

994 There is no higher call

Words and Music: Andy Smith

There is no high-er call, than to live ev-'ry day for the

glo-ry of God. There is no great-er joy,

than sur-ren-der-ing all for a

king-dom that won't pass a-way.

2. Throwing off all that would hinder
   I run for the prize.
   Living my life all for Jesus
   without compromise.
   Your grace, your love
   will keep me from falling;
   I won't be swayed from your higher calling.

995 There is no other name   *(No other name)*

Words and Music: Colin Battersby
arr. Dave Bankhead

There is no o-ther name by which we can be saved,
there is no o-ther name like Je - sus.
You give me joy, you give me peace, you set my spi - rit free,
you lift me up to high - er ground, you're all I need. I'm gon-na
praise you all my days, I'm gon-na fol-low you, there's no

996 There is no other name

Words and Music: Robin Mark

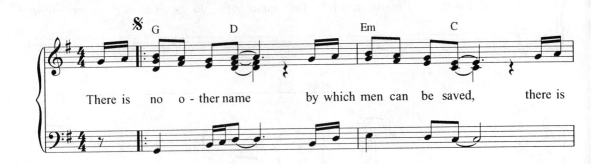

There is no o-ther name by which men can be saved, there is

no o-ther name un-der hea-ven. There is

rest for my soul, and the wound-ed made whole, and the

First time

cap-tives set free and for-gi-ven. There is

997 There's a distant voice *(Into the light)*

Words and Music: David Bird, Richard Lacy and Sarah Lacy
arr. Chris Mitchell

2. Let your heart be clean
   as you search for him
   and seek for what is right,
   for where darkness reigned,
   now the dawn will break
   as you move into the light.

3. Bring your heartfelt thanks
   to the Lord of all,
   in the name of Jesus Christ,
   make righteousness
   and truth your goal
   as children of the light.

998 There's an army

(Lift our voice)

Words and Music: David Jones

1. There's an ar-my rais-ing up a shout of praise, the sound of freedom, hope and li-ber-ty. Migh-ty peo-ple with a pas-sion in their hearts all for Je-sus, King a-bove all kings. Let the earth sing out your name, hear our vic-t'ry shout of praise.

2. There's an army marching out in vict'ry,
   overcomers through the cross of Calvary.
   Darkness trembles at the sound of their voice,
   one in praises they magnify the King.
   Let the earth sing out your name,
   hear the vict'ry shout of praise.

999 There's a new song arising *(New song arising)*

Words and Music: Darrell Evans

One thing I ask of the Lord,
this is what I seek:
that I may dwell in the house of the Lord
all the days of my life,
to gaze upon the beauty of the Lord
and to seek him in his temple.

Psalm 27:4

1000 There's a song

(Be glorified)

Words and Music: David Klassen
arr. Chris Mitchell

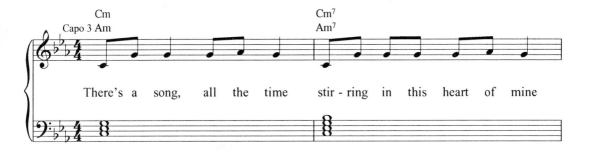

There's a song, all the time stir-ring in this heart of mine

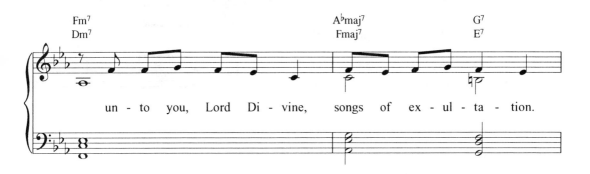

un - to you, Lord Di - vine, songs of ex - ul - ta - tion.

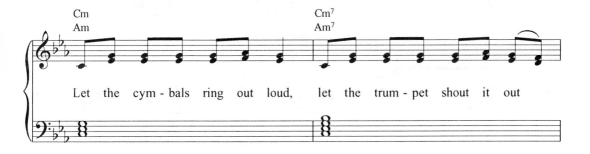

Let the cym - bals ring out loud, let the trum - pet shout it out

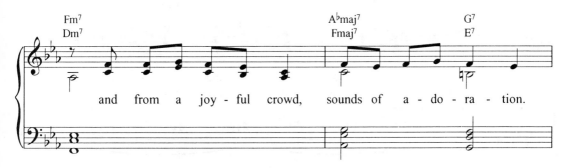

and from a joy - ful crowd, sounds of a - do - ra - tion.

The on-ly One who's wor-thy, re-ceiv-ing all the glo-ry,

your pre-sence right in this place.

Chorus

To you, Lord, who reigns for e - ver,
May the praise in me be pleas - ing,

be my prai - ses now and e - ver.
may your joy be ne - ver ceas - ing,

But the fruit of the Spirit is love, joy, peace,
patience, kindness, goodness, faithfulness,
gentleness and self-control.
Against such things there is no law.

Galatians 5:22-23

1001 There's no one like our God

Words and Music: Vicky Beeching and Steve Mitchinson
arr. Chris Mitchell

There's no one like our God, no one at all.

He gave his Son for us, Je - sus the Lord.

And who can love us like he does? No one at all.

Oh how we love you, Lord.

1. You are high a - bove all na - tions, your glo - ry shines a - bove
2. You lift the need - y from the ash - es and seat them high up with

the hea - vens; hum - bled your - self to love
the prin - ces. You give the bar - ren wo -

and save us: be praised through end - less ge -
- man heal - ing;

- ne - ra - tions.

1002 The Spirit of the Lord

Words and Music: Graham Kendrick

The Spi - rit of the Lord is on me now,

poured out like oil o - ver me.

For the Lord has called and a - noint - ed me

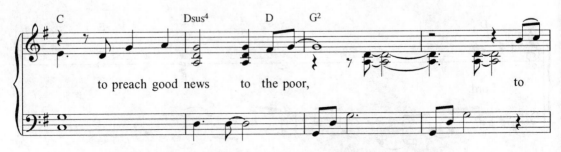

to preach good news to the poor, to

1003 The waves are breaking *(To the ends of the earth)*

Words and Music: Dave Bilbrough

1. The waves are break-ing, the tide is turn-ing, God's Spi-rit is com-ing to this earth; the har-vest is wait-ing, and we have been called to go to the na-tions of this world.

To the ends of the earth, to the ends of the earth, to the ends of the

earth we will go; bear-ing the mes-

-sage that our God can be known, to the ends of the

earth we will go.

2. The fire is falling, the wind is blowing,
   the flame is spreading across our land;
   revival is coming, let the world hear,
   tell ev'ry woman, child and man.

3. The drums are beating, the trumpet is sounding,
   a warrior spirit he's put in our hearts;
   in the name of the Father, Spirit and Son,
   we'll take this word to ev'ryone.

Praise be to the God and Father of our Lord Jesus Christ!
In his great mercy he has given us new birth into a living hope
through the resurrection of Jesus Christ from the dead.

1 Peter 1:3

1004 The wonder of your mercy *(Covenant of grace)*

Words and Music: Don Wallace

The won-der of your mer-cy, Lord, the beau-ty of your

grace, that you would e - ven par-don me

and bring me to this place. I stand be-fore your

ho - li - ness, I can on - ly stand a - mazed:

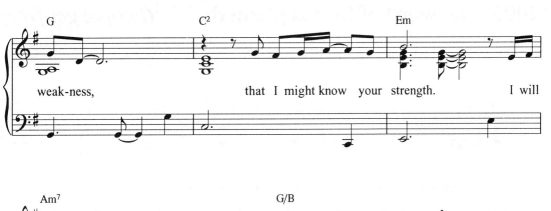

weak-ness,   that I might know your strength.   I will

live   my   life   at   the   cross   of   Christ,   and   raise   a

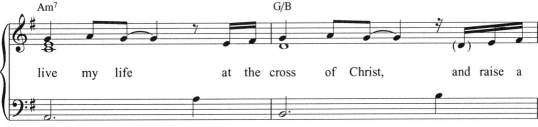

ban - ner   to   pro - claim: the   won - der   of   your

2. You welcome us before you,
   into this holy place;
   the brilliance of your glory
   demands our endless praise.
   The one, the only Saviour
   has opened heaven's doors;
   we can enter in, free from all our sin,
   by your cleansing sacrifice.

1005 The word of God is planted   *(People get free)*

Words and Music: Russell Fragar

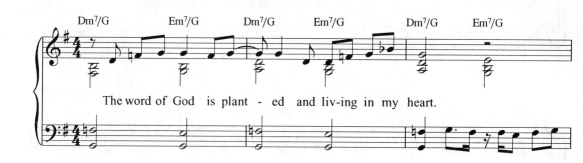

The word of God is plant - ed and liv-ing in my heart.

I'm an o - ver-com - er, I live his pro-mise

out.   This was not   a new

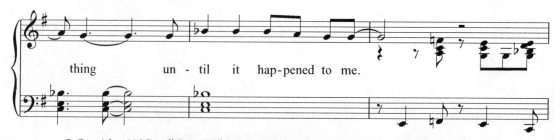

thing   un - til   it hap-pened to me.

1006 The world's shaking with the love of God
(My glorious)

Words and Music: Martin Smith and Stuart Garrard
arr. Chris Mitchell

1. The world's shak - ing with the love of God,
2. Clouds are break - ing, hea - ven's come to earth,

great and glo - rious, let the whole earth
hearts a - wake - ning, let the church bells

sing, and all you e - ver do is change
ring,

the old for new, peo - ple we be - lieve that:

God is big - ger than the air we breathe, the world we'll

1007 This is the air I breathe

(Breathe)

Words and Music: Marie Barnett
arr. Chris Mitchell

This is   the air   I breathe,
This is   my dai - ly bread,

this is   the air   I breathe;
this is   my dai - ly bread;

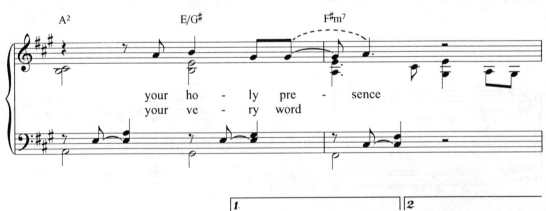

your ho - ly pre - sence
your ve - ry word

liv - ing   in me.
spo - ken   to me.   And I,

I'm des-p'rate for you.

And I, I'm lost with-out

you.

'But what about you?' he asked. 'Who do you say I am?'
Simon Peter answered,
'You are the Christ, the Son of the living God.'

Matthew 16:15-16

1008 This is the place

(Holy ground)

Words and Music: Dave Bilbrough

2. Your fire burns but never dies;
   I realise this is holy ground.

3. The great 'I Am' revealed to man;
   take off your shoes, this is holy ground.

1009 This is the year

Words and Music: Graham Kendrick
arr. Dave Bankhead

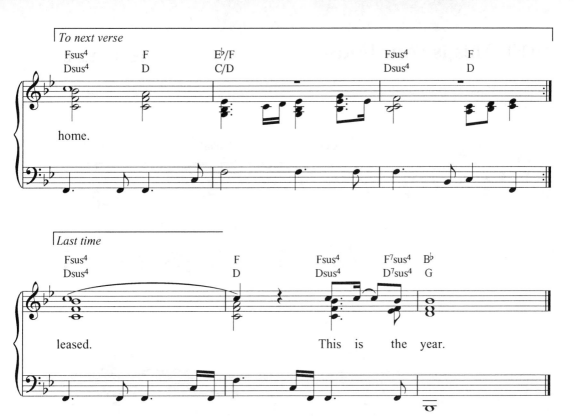

2. This is the year of joy for tears
   and beauty out of ashes.
   When skies will clear if we will share,
   forgive and learn what love is.
   Let's crown the year with kindness
   and live in peace;
   fill all the world with songs
   that never cease.

3. These are the days of heaven's grace
   and favour smiling on us.
   Two thousand years of hopes and prayers
   are met in one great chorus.
   A light has dawned upon us
   and will increase,
   and countless captive souls
   shall be released.

1010 This is your house

Words and Music: Graham Kendrick
arr. Richard Lewis

This is your house, and we your peo-ple, the

ob - ject of your love, pur-chased by your blood. We are

liv - ing stones built to - ge - ther to re - veal

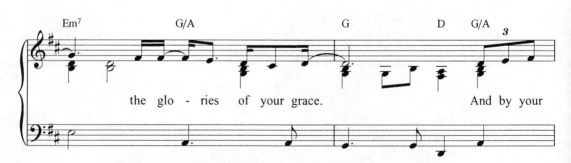

the glo - ries of your grace. And by your

Fill your house with prayer for all the na - tions, to your house of bles - sing let the na - tions run, to wor-ship Je - sus, O let the peo - ple come.

1011 This song in my heart

(Free to dance)

Words and Music: Darlene Zschech
arr. Dave Bankhead

This song in my heart, this song in my soul, this song I was born to sing.

It's your song of free-dom, now I'm free to dance a-gain.

I'll sing in the dark-ness, I'll laugh in the rain, re-

joice in your love a-gain. It's your song of free-dom, now I'm

your ho - ly name. Je - sus, I'll

dance be- fore your throne, bring this hea- ven- ly sound to you a - lone.

This song wi- thin me, Lord, will bless your ho - ly name.

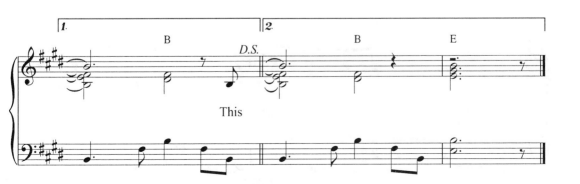

This

1012 This yearning deep within me *(Have your way)*

Words and Music: Darlene Zschech

1. This yearn-ing deep with-in me reaches out to you.
   need you, Ho-ly Spi-rit, fire to my soul.

Your oil of joy for mourn-ing
Con-sume my to-tal be-ing,

soaks me, makes me new. And I will go to your sec-
Je-sus, take con-trol.

-ret place, bow my knee to your glo-

1013 Those who wait on the Lord *(Wait on the Lord)*

Words and Music: David Klassen
arr. Chris Mitchell

Chorus

Those who wait on the Lord shall mount up with wings as ea-gles, shall walk and they shall not faint.

In the strength of our God we'll run and we'll not grow wea-ry if we wait on the Lord.

Last time to Coda

we wait on the Lord. We'll fly so much high - er, high-

- er and high - er. Our strength will be more than be - fore

'cause we'll fly with the Fa - ther, he'll give the pow - er to o-

- ver - come. Wait on the Lord. - ver - come.

Those who wait on the Lord shall mount up with wings

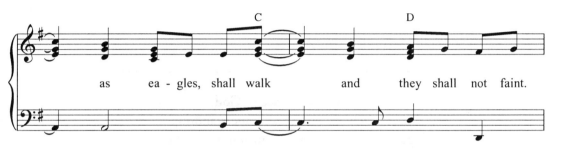

as ea - gles, shall walk and they shall not faint.

In the strength of our God we'll run and we'll not

grow wea - ry if we wait on the Lord. we wait on the Lord.

And the peace of God,
which transcends all understanding,
will guard your hearts and your minds in Christ Jesus.

Philippians 4:7

1014 Thou art worthy, great Jehovah

Words and Music: Karen Eagen
arr. Chris Mitchell

Thou art wor - thy, great Je - ho - vah.

Thou art wor - thy, migh - ty God.

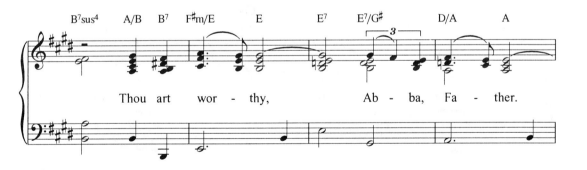

Thou art wor - thy, Ab - ba, Fa - ther.

Thou art wor - thy, Lamb of God.

1015 Thou didst leave thy throne

Words: Emily Elizabeth Steele Elliot, based on Luke 2:7, adapted by Michael Forster

Music: Timothy Richard Matthews

MARGARET 10 8 11 8 and Refrain

1. Thou didst leave thy throne and thy king-ly crown when thou cam-est to earth for

me, but in Beth-le-hem's home was there found no room for thy

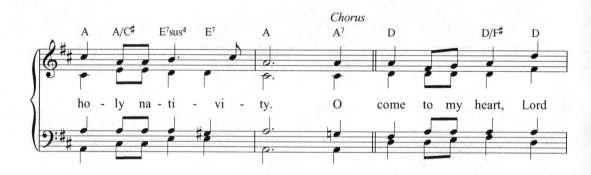

ho-ly na-ti-vi-ty. *Chorus* O come to my heart, Lord

Je-sus, there is room in my heart for thee.

2. Heaven's arches rang when the angels sang
   and proclaimed thee of royal degree,
   but in lowliest birth didst thou come to earth
   and in deepest humility.

3. Though the fox found rest, and the bird its nest
   in the shade of the cedar tree,
   yet the world found no bed for the Saviour's head
   in the desert of Galilee.

4. Though thou camest, Lord, with the living word
   that should set all thy people free,
   yet with treachery, scorn and a crown of thorn
   did they bear thee to Calvary.

5. When the heav'ns shall ring and the angels sing
   at thy coming to victory,
   let thy voice call me home, saying, 'Heav'n has room,
   there is room at my side for thee.'

The Lord is my shepherd, I shall not be in want.
He makes me lie down in green pastures,
he leads me beside quiet waters.

Psalm 23:1-2

1016 Though trials will come
(Consider it joy)

Words and Music: Graham Kendrick
arr. Richard Lewis

1. Though trials will come, don't fear, don't run. Lift up your
2. Though trials will come, won't fear, won't run. We'll lift up our

eyes, hold fast, be strong. Have faith, keep on be-liev-
eyes, hold fast, be strong. Have faith, keep on be-liev-

- ing. Lift up your eyes for God is at
- ing. We'll lift up our eyes for God is at

(1&2) work in us, mould-ing and shap-ing us out of his
(3) trust-ing him, rea-dy for a-ny-thing, 'til we're com-

1017 Thou, O Lord, art a shield about me

(A shield about me)

Words and Music: Donn Thomas and Charles Williams
arr. Chris Mitchell

Thou, O Lord, art a shield a-

bout me; you're my glo - ry, you're the lift - er of my

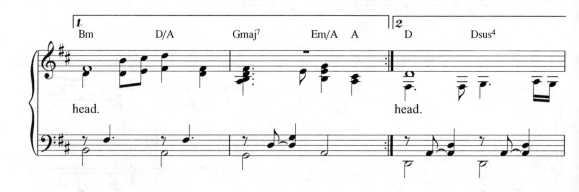

head. head.

Hal - le - lu - jah! Hal - le-

lu - jah! Hal - le - lu - jah! You're the

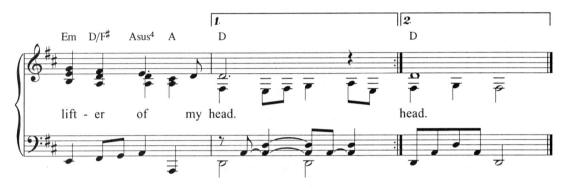

lift - er of my head. head.

Be imitators of God, therefore,
as dearly loved children
and live a life of love,
just as Christ loved us
and gave himself up for us
as a fragrant offering and sacrifice to God.

Ephesians 5:1-2

1018 Thou who wast rich beyond all splendour

Words: Bishop Frank Houghton

Music: French carol melody
harm. by Charles Herbert Kitson.

FRAGRANCE 98 98 98

2. Thou who art God beyond all praising,
all for love's sake becamest Man;
stooping so low, but sinners raising
heav'nwards by thine eternal plan.
Thou who art God beyond all praising,
all for love's sake becamest Man.

3. Thou whou art love beyond all telling,
Saviour and King, we worship thee.
Emmanuel, within us dwelling,
make us what thou wouldst have us be.
Thou who art love beyond all telling,
Saviour and King, we worship thee.

1019 Through days of rage and wonder

Words and Music: Graham Kendrick

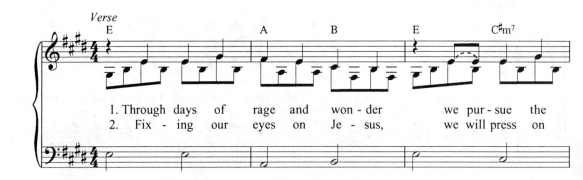

1. Through days of rage and won-der we pur-sue the
2. Fix-ing our eyes on Je-sus, we will press on

end of time, to seize the day e-ter-nal,
day by day; this world's vain pas-sing plea-sures

the reign of love di-vine.
are not our des-ti-ny.

Our an-cient

rites of pas-sage still are the bread and

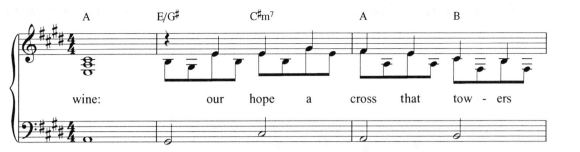

wine: our hope a cross that tow - ers

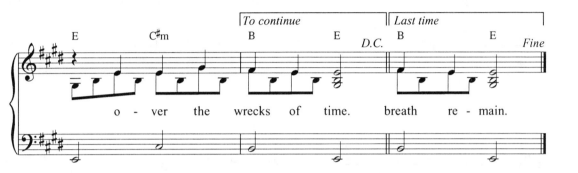

o - ver the wrecks of time. breath re - main.

3. Through days of rage and wonder,
   by the awesome pow'r of prayer
   God will shake ev'ry nation,
   secrets will be laid bare.
   And if his light increasing
   casts deeper shadows here,
   safe in his holy presence,
   love will cast out our fear.

4. Through days of rage and wonder
   you will give us grace to stand
   and seek a heav'nly city
   not built by human hands.
   Now is the only moment
   within our pow'r to change:
   to give back in obedience
   while life and breath remain.

1020 Through the cross   *(Healing river)*

Words and Music: Mike Burn

1. Through the cross, Je-sus you tri-umphed, by your blood you bought our

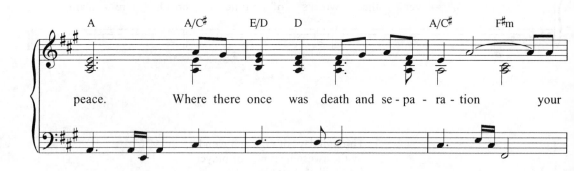

peace. Where there once was death and se-pa-ra-tion your

heal - ing ri - ver flows. Let it flow, let it

flow, let the heal - ing ri - ver flow. Gra-cious

God, we cry to you: let the heal - ing ri - ver flow.

1, 2, 3. | *Last time*

2. Bind up
3. Break down
4. May your

2. Bind up wounds within our homes, Lord,
   reconcile husbands and wives.
   Turn the fathers' hearts towards their children,
   O, let the river flow.

3. Break down walls of isolation,
   rescue those who live in fear.
   May the lonely find love in your fam'ly,
   O, let the river flow.

4. May your church rise up as one now,
   join the streams in one accord.
   Young and old will stand and sing with one voice
   to praise our risen Lord.

1021 To God be the glory

(My tribute)

Words and Music: Andraé Crouch

1022 To him who sits on the throne

Words and Music: Debbye Graafsma

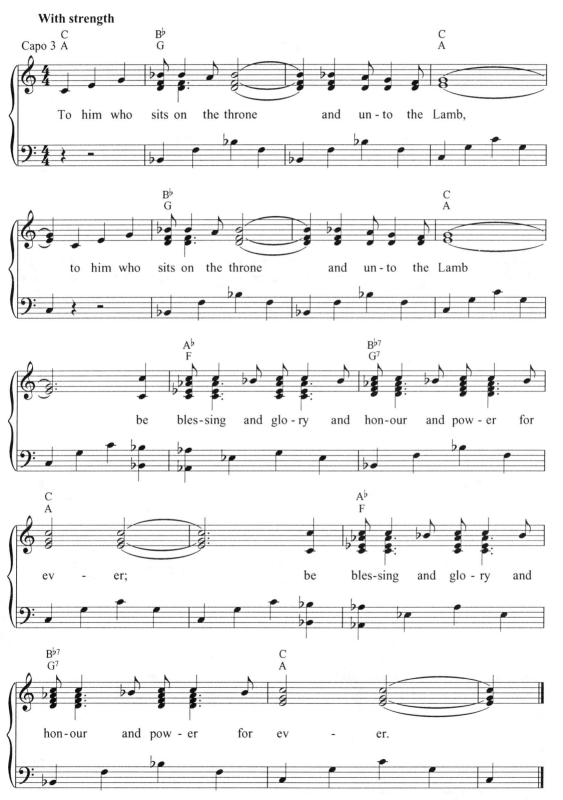

With strength

To him who sits on the throne and un-to the Lamb,

to him who sits on the throne and un-to the Lamb

be bles-sing and glo-ry and hon-our and pow-er for

ev - er; be bles-sing and glo-ry and

hon-our and pow - er for ev - er.

1023 To the King eternal

Words and Music: Graham Kendrick

Dear friends, let us love one another,
for love comes from God.
Everyone who loves
has been born of God and knows God.

Dear friends, since God so loved us,
we also ought to love one another.

1 John 4:7, 11

1024 Turn the hearts of the fathers   *(Heal our land)*

Words and Music: Liz Fitzgibbon

With emotion

1. Turn the hearts of the fa - thers to the hearts of the child - ren, O
\- pair what is bro - ken, in the heart, in the spi - rit, O

Lord, come and heal, heal our land. Take the pain, take the shame of the
Lord, come and heal, heal our land. Re - stor - ing the fa - thers in the

past ge - ne - ra - tion, O Lord, come and heal, heal our land. Lord, heal our
heart of the na - tion, O Lord, come and heal, heal our land.

land; O Lord, heal our land, heal our land, O Lord, heal our

3. We are fathered by you,
   you are faithful and true,
   restore and renew what is lost.
   Change the face of this land,
   touch with your tender hand,
   O Lord, come and heal, heal our land.

4. Son of righteousness,
   come arise over us,
   O Lord, come and heal, heal our land.
   With healing in your wings,
   your love changes all things,
   O Lord, come and heal, heal our land.

The Lord reigns,
let the nations tremble;
he sits enthroned between the cherubim,
let the earth shake.
Great is the Lord in Zion;
he is exalted over all the nations.

Psalm 99:1-2

1025 Under the shadow

Words and Music: Carol Mundy

you are my Fa - ther; and in your arms
your prai - ses I'll sing; thank you God

I will a - bide. Un-der the sha -
for be - ing my King.

1026 We are a moment

(Be unto your name)

Words and Music: Lynn DeShazo and Gary Sadler

We are a mo-ment, you are for e-ver, Lord of the a-ges, God be-fore time.

We are a va-pour, you are e-ter-nal, love e-ver-last-ing, reign-ing on high.

Therefore, I urge you, brothers,
in view of God's mercy,
to offer your bodies as living sacrifices,
holy and pleasing to God –
this is your spiritual act of worship.

Romans 12:1

1027 We ask you, O Lord

(The latter rain)

Words and Music: Richard Lewis

To continue

Send your rain, mer-cy from hea-ven, send your rain, the grace of your Son. Send your rain, Word of your pow - er, send your rain, come fill ev - 'ry-one. Send your

Repeat ad lib, then D.S. al Fine

1028 We bow down

Words and Music: Viola Grafstrom

1029 We come into your presence
(That's what we came here for)

Words and Music: Russell Fragar
and Darlene Zschech

We come in-to your pre-sence with sing - ing, come in-to your pre-sence with praise, and en - ter your gates with thank-ful hearts; we are going to ce - le-brate. All of hea-ven's wait-ing, pow'r is on its way, so we shout 'hal-le-lu-jah', lift - ing to you a migh-ty roar of praise.

1030 We come to you with a heart of thanks
(All creation)

Words and Music: Brian Doerksen and Steve Mitchison
arr. Chris Mitchell

1. We come to you with a heart of thanks, for your love. To
2. We come to you with a song of praise, for your love. The

be a liv – ing sac – ri – fice, brought with love. We
mu – sic of our soul's de – light, brought with love. We

come to you with a heart of thanks, for your love; an
come to you with a song of praise, for your love.

of – fer-ing of all we are, brought with love.
Sounds of joy and grate – ful – ness, brought with love.

1031 We have a vision

Words and Music: Chris Falson

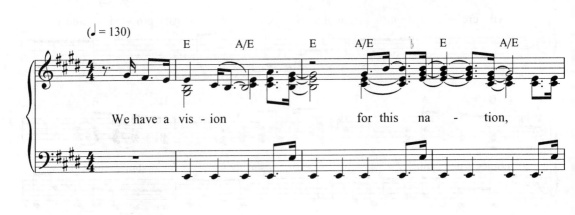

We have a vis - ion for this na - tion,

we share a dream for this land,

we join with an - gels

in ce - le - bra - tion, by faith we speak re - vi -

Who is a God like you,
who pardons sin
and forgives the transgression
of the remnant of his inheritance?
You do not stay angry for ever
but delight to show mercy.

Micah 7:18

1032 We have come

Words and Music: Janine Price
arr. Dave Bankhead

We have come just to praise our awe-some Fa - ther in this place.

It's his love that makes us sing, he's be - come our ev - 'ry - thing.

So let us dance be - fore him, and make a joy - ful noise,

1033 We have come into his house

Words and Music: Bruce Ballinger
arr. Chris Mitchell

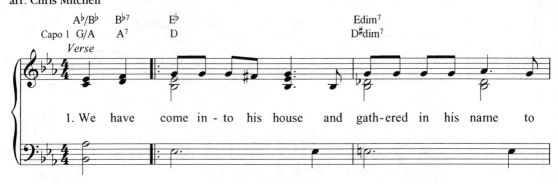

1. We have come in-to his house and gath-ered in his name to

wor - ship him. We have come in-to his house and

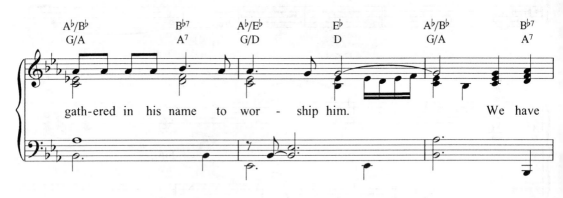

gath-ered in his name to wor - ship him. We have

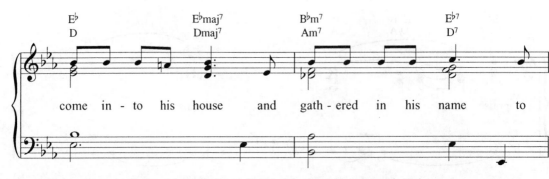

come in - to his house and gath - ered in his name to

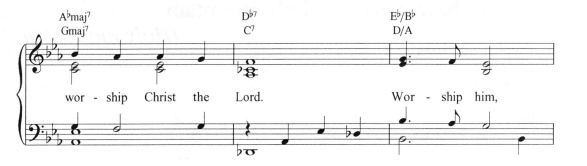

wor - ship Christ the Lord. Wor - ship him,

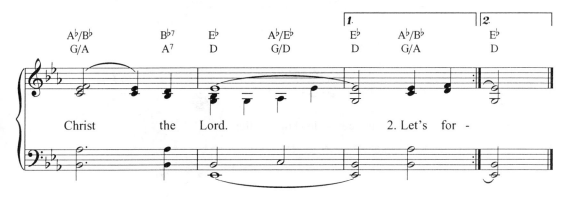

Christ the Lord. 2. Let's for -

2. Let's forget about ourselves
   and magnify his name
   and worship him.
   Let's forget about ourselves
   and magnify his name
   and worship him.
   Let's forget about ourselves
   and magnify his name
   and worship Christ the Lord.
   Worship him, Christ the Lord.

1034 We have come to a holy mountain

(Holy mountain)

Words and Music: Russ Hughes
arr. Richard Lewis

(♩ = 94)

1. We have come to a ho - ly moun - tain, join - ing an - gels in ce - le - bra - tion, a thous - and thous - and lift their voi - ces as the first - born Church sings her prai - ses to the Ho - ly One, to the Ho - ly One.

O Ho - ly God, we have come to you, con-sum-ing

fire to be re-fined in you, O Ho-ly One, how we long

2nd time to Coda ⊕

for you, our one de - sire is found in you.

3. We have come to a ho - ly moun - tain,

not in fear but with re - joic - ing; a

1035 We have come to a throne of grace

(King of grace)

Words and Music: Mark Altrogge

1. We have come to a throne of grace, where our migh-ty Sa-viour per-fects our praise; where wrath and judge-ment have been put a-way, where not a trace of all our sin re-mains. You're the

2. We have come to a throne of grace,
   where our Prince of Peace ever lives,
   to pray for those his sacrifice has bought and saved,
   where saints and angels sing eternal praise.

1036 We have come to worship the Lord

Words and Music: David Horton
arr. Chris Mitchell

We have come to wor-ship the Lord,

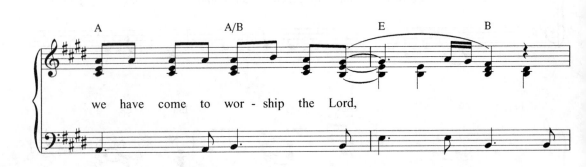

we have come to wor-ship the Lord,

bow down be-fore him, love and a-dore him,

we have come to wor-ship the Lord.

Verse

Enter in, in the Holy Place; enter

in, and look upon his face; he is

wor - thy, he is ho - ly, he is

won - der - ful, enter in.

1037 We have sung our songs of victory   *(How long?)*

Words and Music: Stuart Townend

1. We have sung our songs of vic-t'ry, we have prayed to you for rain; we have cried for your com-pas-sion to re-new the land a-gain. Now we're standing in your pre-sence, more hun-gry than be-fore; now we're on your steps of mer-cy, and we're knock-ing at your door. How long be-fore you drench the bar-ren land? How long

2. Lord, we know your heart is broken
   by the evil that you see,
   and you've stayed your hand of judgement
   for you plan to set men free.
   But the land is still in darkness,
   and we've fled from what is right;
   we have failed the silent children
   who will never see the light.

3. But I know a day is coming
   when the deaf will hear his voice,
   when the blind will see their Saviour,
   and the lame will leap for joy;
   when the widow finds a husband
   who will always love his bride,
   and the orphan finds a father
   who will never leave her side.

Final Chorus:
How long before your glory lights the skies?
How long before your radiance lifts our eyes?
How long before your fragrance fills the air?
How long before the earth resounds with songs of joy?

1038 We lift our hands to worship you

Words and Music: Steve and Velveta Thompson
arr. Chris Mitchell

1. We lift our hands to wor - ship you, we

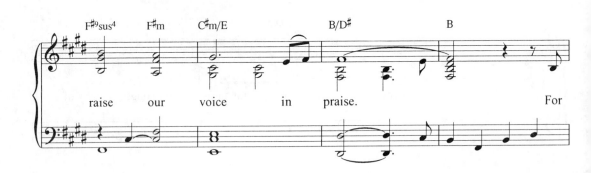

raise our voice in praise. For

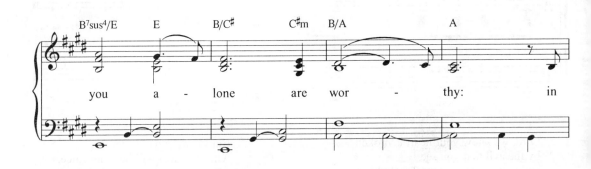

you a - lone are wor - thy: in

maj - es - ty you reign. We

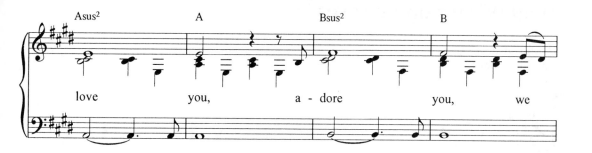

love you, a - dore you, we

bow down be - fore you. 2. We

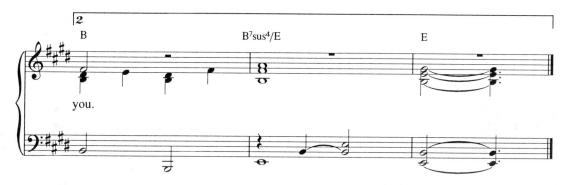

you.

2. We stand in awe before you,
   we worship at your feet.
   Your holiness surrounds us,
   your beauty, Lord, we see.

1039 We lift up our eyes

Words and Music: Isi de Gersigny
based on Psalm 121

1040 We're a bright light together

Words and Music: Capt. Alan Price, CA
arr. B. Chesser

We're a bright light to-ge-ther, with the light of Je-sus we

shine; we're a grand band to-ge-ther, with

our friend Je-sus it's fine. We're a swell smell to-

ge-ther, it's the fra-grance of Je-sus we share! When-

e-ver we are to-ge-ther, Je-sus is spe-cial-ly

Last time to Coda

1041 We're looking to your promise *(Send revival)*

Words and Music: Matt Redman

1042 We're so thankful to you   *(Thank you, Lord)*

Words and Music: Chris Cartwright and Richard Lewis

1. We're so thank-ful to you, we're so grate-ful for the things you've done, that you died for us on the cross such a pain-ful death, that you paid the price for us, you paid the price for us. And we say thank you, Lord. We say thank you,

Lord. We say thank you for what you have

done. And we say thank you, Lord. We say

thank you, Lord. We say thank you for the things you have

done. 2. It's so

2. It's so wonderful that you rose,
   victorious over death and hell.
   All authority is now yours,
   and the Comforter
   you have sent in fullness to us,
   you have come to us.

1043 We rest on thee

Words: Edith Gilling Cherry

Music: Jean Sibelius

FINLANDIA 11 10 11 10 11 10

1. We rest on thee, our shield and our de- fend- er!

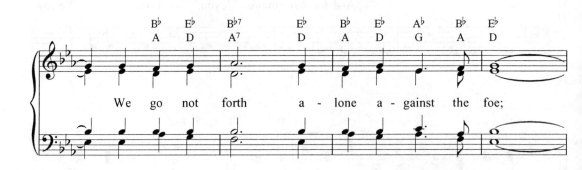

We go not forth a - lone a - gainst the foe;

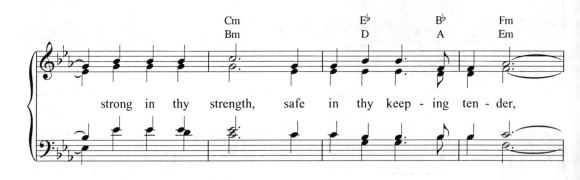

strong in thy strength, safe in thy keep - ing ten - der,

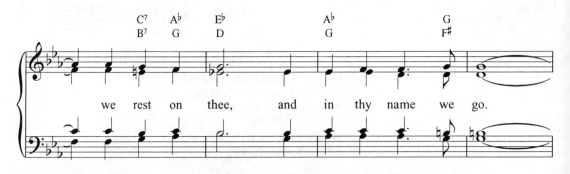

we rest on thee, and in thy name we go.

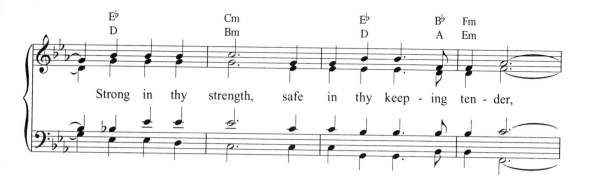

Strong in thy strength, safe in thy keep - ing ten - der,

we rest on thee, and in thy name we go.

2. Yes, in thy name, O captain of salvation!
   In thy dear name, all other names above;
   Jesus our righteousness, our sure foundation,
   our prince of glory and our king of love.
   Jesus our righteousness, our sure foundation,
   our prince of glory and our king of love.

3. We go in faith, our own great weakness feeling,
   and needing more each day thy grace to know:
   yet from our hearts a song of triumph pealing,
   'We rest on thee, and in thy name we go.'
   Yet from our hearts a song of triumph pealing,
   'We rest on thee, and in thy name we go.'

4. We rest on thee, our shield and our defender!
   Thine is the battle, thine shall be the praise;
   when passing through the gates of pearly splendour,
   victors, we rest with thee, through endless days.
   When passing through the gates of pearly splendour,
   victors, we rest with thee, through endless days.

My soul glorifies the Lord
and my spirit rejoices in God my Saviour.

Luke 1:46b-47

1044 We will give ourselves no rest
(Knocking on the door of heaven)

Words and Music: Matt Redman
and Steve Cantellow arr. Chris Mitchell

We will give our-selves no rest 'til your king-dom comes

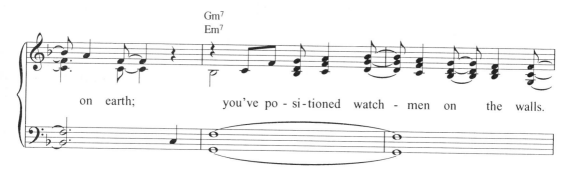

on earth; you've po-si-tioned watch-men on the walls.

Now our prayers will flow

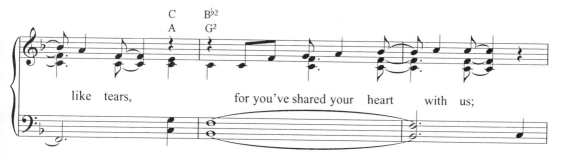

like tears, for you've shared your heart with us;

God of hea-ven, on our knees we fall.

Come down in pow-er, re -

veal your heart a - gain; come hear our

cries, the tears that plead for rain. We're

1045 We will never be the same

Words and Music: Michael Battersby

We will ne-ver be the same, we've been touched by your love,
ne-ver go-ing back a-gain, we've been washed by your blood.
Deep calls, deep calls to deep,
and you're clo - ser than a bro-ther, you've put your life
in - side of me, now I'm free for e - ver.

You are the Lord of my life, my rea-son for liv - ing.

You are my day and my night. That's why I'm giv - ing all

to you, 'cause when all is said and done

we will ne-ver be the same be-cause of you.

1046 We will seek your face
(Touching heaven, changing earth)

Words and Music: Reuben Morgan

We will seek your face, al-migh-ty God,
Fa-ther, let re-vi-val start in us,

turn and pray for you to heal our land.
then ev-'ry heart will know your king-dom come.

Lift-ing up the name of the Lord, in pow-er and in u-ni-ty.

We will see the na-tions turn. Touch-ing hea-ven, chang-

2. Never looking back we'll run the race,
   giving you our lives
   we'll gain the prize.
   We will take the harvest given us,
   though we sow in tears,
   we'll reap in joy.

1047 What a fellowship
(Leaning on the everlasting arms)

Words: Elisha A. Hoffman

Music: Anthony J. Showalter

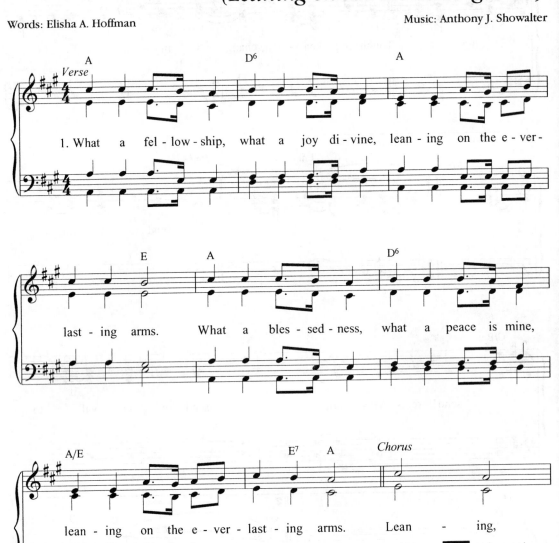

1. What a fel - low - ship, what a joy di - vine, lean - ing on the e - ver-

last - ing arms. What a bles - sed - ness, what a peace is mine,

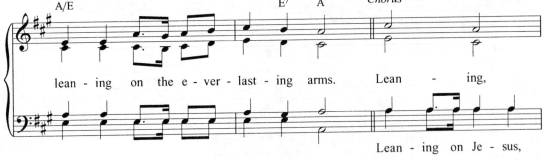

lean - ing on the e - ver - last - ing arms. Lean - ing,

Lean - ing on Je - sus,

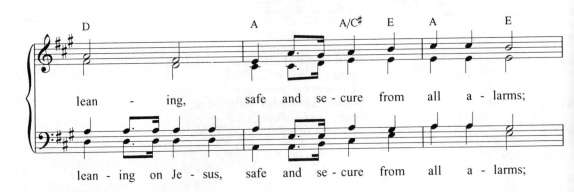

lean - ing, safe and se - cure from all a - larms;

lean - ing on Je - sus, safe and se - cure from all a - larms;

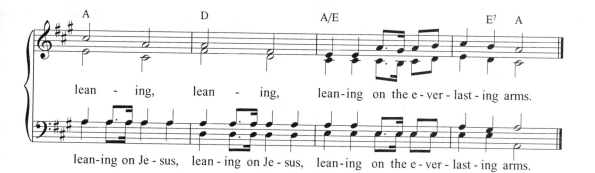

lean - ing, lean - ing, lean-ing on the e - ver - last - ing arms.

lean-ing on Je - sus, lean - ing on Je - sus, lean-ing on the e - ver - last - ing arms.

2. O how sweet to walk in this pilgrim way,
   leaning on the everlasting arms.
   O how bright the path grows from day to day,
   leaning on the everlasting arms.

3. What have I to dread, what have I to fear,
   leaning on the everlasting arms?
   I have blessèd peace with my Lord so near,
   leaning on the everlasting arms.

If I speak in the tongues of men and of angels,
but have not love,
I am only a resounding gong or a clanging cymbal.
If I have the gift of prophecy
and can fathom all mysteries and all knowledge,
and if I have a faith that can move mountains,
but have not love,
I am nothing.
If I give all I possess to the poor
and surrender my body to the flames,
but have not love,
I gain nothing.
Love is patient, love is kind.
It does not envy, it does not boast, it is not proud.
It is not rude, it is not self-seeking,
it is not easily angered, it keeps no record of wrongs.
Love does not delight in evil
but rejoices with the truth.
It always protects, always trusts,
always hopes, always perseveres.

1 Corinthians 13:1-7

1048 What a healing, Jesus

Words and Music: Mary Brown
arr. Richard Lewis

What a heal - ing, Je - sus, I've found in you. What a

heal - ing, Je - sus, you re - store, re - fresh and re - new. You're my

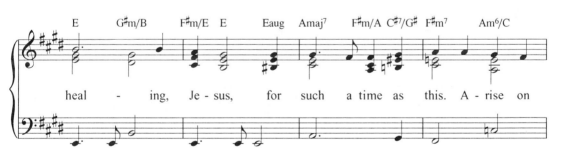

heal - ing, Je - sus, for such a time as this. A - rise on

heal - ing wings, Son of Right - eous - ness.

1049 What a hope you've treasured up for us
(Great and precious promises)

Words and Music: Mark Altrogge
arr. Dave Bankhead

1. What a hope you've trea-sured up for us, wealth and rich-es hid-den in Je-sus. What a won-drous gift to be in-vi-ted to your throne, to find mer-cy and grace in our need.

Chorus
Such great and pre-cious pro-mi-ses you've gi-ven,

2. The faithfulness you've shown us in the past,
   assures us of your goodness in the future.
   You who did not spare your Son,
   but gave him for us all,
   you will surely give us all other things.

'Come now, let us reason together,'
says the Lord.
'Though your sins are like scarlet,
they shall be as white as snow;
though they are red as crimson,
they shall be like wool.'

Isaiah 1:18

1050 What a mighty God we serve

Words and Music: unknown
arr. Chris Mitchell

What a migh - ty God we serve,

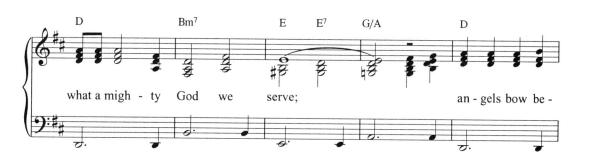

what a migh - ty God we serve; an - gels bow be -

fore him, hea-ven and earth a - dore him, what a migh - ty

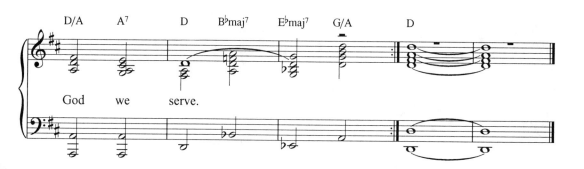

God we serve.

1051 What can wash away my sin?
(Nothing but the blood)

Words and Music: Robert Lowry
arr. Chris Mitchell

1. What can wash a - way my sin? No-thing but the blood of

Je - sus. What can make me whole a - gain?

No-thing but the blood of Je - sus. O, pre - cious

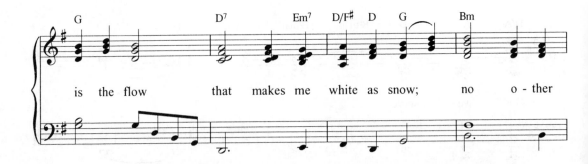

is the flow that makes me white as snow; no o - ther

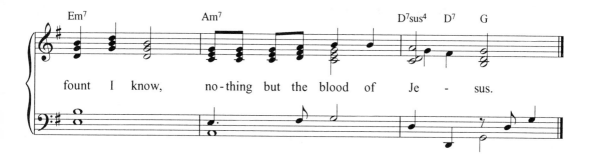

fount I know, no-thing but the blood of Je - sus.

2. For my pardon this I see,
   nothing but the blood of Jesus;
   for my cleansing, this my plea:
   nothing but the blood of Jesus.

3. Nothing can for sin atone,
   nothing but the blood of Jesus;
   naught of good that I have done,
   nothing but the blood of Jesus.

4. This is all my hope and peace,
   nothing but the blood of Jesus;
   this is all my righteousness,
   nothing but the blood of Jesus.

1052 What to say, Lord?

(Every day)

Words and Music: Joel Houston
arr. Dave Bankhead

1. What to say, Lord? It's you who gave me life and I
2. Ev-'ry day, Lord, I'll learn to stand up-on your word.

can't ex-plain just how much you mean to me now
And I pray that I, that I may come to know you more,

that you have saved me, Lord. I give all that I am to you,
that you would guide me in ev-'ry sin-gle step I take, that

that ev-'ry day I can be a light that shines your
ev-'ry day I can

name.

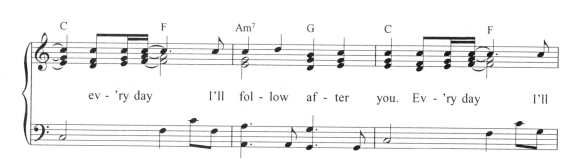

be your light un-to the world. Ev-'ry day it's you I live for,

ev-'ry day I'll fol-low af-ter you. Ev-'ry day I'll

walk with you, my Lord. Lord.

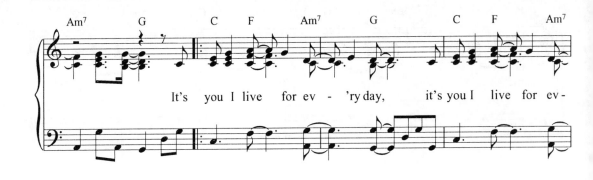

It's you I live for ev - 'ry day, it's you I live for ev-

- 'ry day, it's you I live for ev - 'ry day.

It's

Through Jesus, therefore, let us continually
offer to God a sacrifice of praise
– the fruit of lips that confess his name.

Hebrews 13:15

1053 When I pray

(Fire fall)

Words and Music: Richard Lewis

and the Dev - il can not stand when I pray.

Fi - re fall! Fi - re fall!

And re - lease the king - dom of the liv - ing God.

Fi - re fall!

2. For my praise, it burns like incense,
   and my prayers rise to your throne;
   they release fire from the altar,
   and the Devil cannot stand,
   and the Devil cannot stand,
   and the Devil cannot stand when I pray.

I will extol the Lord at all times;
his praise will always be on my lips.
My soul will boast in the Lord;
let the afflicted hear and rejoice.
Glorify the Lord with me:
let us exalt his name together.

Psalm 34:1-3

1054 When morning gilds the skies

Words: German (19th century)
trans. Edward Caswall

Music: Joseph Barnby

LAUDES DOMINI 6 6 6 D

1. When morn-ing gilds the skies, my heart a-wak-ing cries, may Je-sus Christ be praised. A-like at work and prayer to Je-sus I re-pair; may Je-sus Christ be praised.

2. The night becomes as day,
   when from the heart we say:
   may Jesus Christ be praised.
   The pow'rs of darkness fear,
   when this sweet chant they hear:
   may Jesus Christ be praised.

3. In heav'n's eternal bliss
   the loveliest strain is this:
   may Jesus Christ be praised.
   Let air, and sea, and sky
   from depth to height reply:
   may Jesus Christ be praised.

4. Be this, while life is mine,
   my canticle divine:
   may Jesus Christ be praised.
   Be this th'eternal song
   through all the ages on:
   may Jesus Christ be praised.

1055 When the cares of life come   *(Only you for me)*

Words and Music: Steve and Vikki Cook

1. When the cares of life come and dark-en my eyes;
there's on-ly you for me. When my heart grows
cold you bring fire to my soul; there's on-ly you for
me. You're all I de-sire, Lord, you're all I
need. *Chorus* I want on-ly you for me.

2. When the way is hard and the valley dark;
   there's only you for me.
   In my deepest loss I will cling to the cross;
   there's only you for me.
   In love's sov'reign hand is all I could need.

3. As I run the race I will hope in your grace;
   there's only you for me.
   When my flesh has failed and I step through the veil;
   there's only you for me.
   And I'll fully know that you're all I need.

1056 When the darkness fills my senses
(Your unfailing love)

Words and Music: Reuben Morgan

When the dark - ness fills my sen - ses, when my blind - ness keeps me from your touch, Je - sus, come.

When my bur - den keeps me doubt - ing, when my mem - 'ries take the place of you, Je - sus, come.

1057 When upon life's billows you are tempest-tossed
(Count your blessings)

Words: Johnson Oatman, Jr.

Music: Edwin O. Excell
arr. Chris Mitchell

Verse

1. When up-on life's bil-lows you are tem-pest-tossed,
when you are dis-cou-raged, think-ing all is lost,
count your ma-ny bles-sings, name them one by one,
and it will sur-prise you what the Lord has done.

Chorus

Count your bles-sings, name them one by one;

count your bles - sings, see what God has done.

Count your bles-sings, name them one by one;

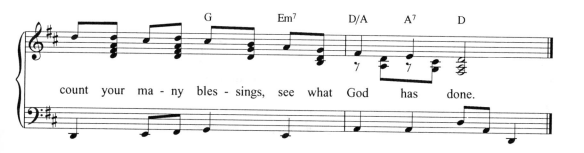

count your ma - ny bles - sings, see what God has done.

2. Are you ever burdened with a load of care?
   Does the cross seem heavy you are called to bear?
   Count your many blessings; ev'ry doubt will fly,
   and you will be singing as the days go by.

3. When you look at others with their lands and gold,
   think that Christ has promised you his wealth untold;
   count your many blessings; money cannot buy
   your reward in heaven nor your home on high.

4. So amid the conflict, whether great or small,
   do not be discouraged; God is over all.
   Count your many blessings; angels will attend,
   help and comfort give you to your journey's end.

1058 Where the Spirit is there is liberty
(Lifted me high again)

Words and Music: Reuben Morgan
arr. Chris Mitchell

1. Where the Spi - rit is there is li - ber-ty, full - ness of joy.
2. You are awe - some in this place, O Lord, we ex-alt your name.

With a heart of praise I will lift my voice in the ho - ly place.
For the hope you set in - side of me, I will e - ver sing.

Chorus

Your love has lift - ed me up a-gain, now I'm free to live.

My heart is steadfast, O God,
my heart is steadfast;
I will sing and make music.
Awake, my soul!
Awake, harp and lyre!
I will awaken the dawn.

Psalm 57:7-8

1059 While shepherds watched

Words: Nahum Tate, alt.

Music: from Este's *Psalter* (1592)

WINCHESTER OLD CM

1. While shepherds watched their flocks by night, all seated on the ground, the angel of the Lord came down, and glory shone around.

2. 'Fear not,' said he, (for mighty dread
   had seized their troubled mind);
   'glad tidings of great joy I bring
   to you and all mankind.

3. 'To you in David's town this day
   is born of David's line
   a Saviour, who is Christ the Lord;
   and this shall be the sign:

4. 'The heav'nly babe you there shall find
   to human view displayed,
   all meanly wrapped in swathing bands,
   and in a manger laid.'

5. Thus spake the seraph, and forthwith
   appeared a shining throng
   of angels praising God, who thus
   addressed their joyful song:

6. 'All glory be to God on high,
   and to the earth be peace,
   goodwill henceforth from heav'n to earth
   begin and never cease.'

1060 Whiter than the snow

Words and Music: Mike Burn

Whi-ter than the snow, pur-er than the clear-est stream; wash me and I'll be bathed in pu-ri-ty, I long to feel clean. A robe of right-eous-ness, a robe that I could not af-ford; my Lord, you paid the price, your per-fect sac-ri-

The sacrifices of God are a broken spirit;
a broken and contrite heart,
O God, you will not despise.

Psalm 51:17

1061 Who compares to your matchless beauty?
(Only God for me)

Words and Music: Gary Sadler

2. Who could show me a heart so faithful?
   What could give me a joy so deep,
   O Lord, my Lord?
   Who could open the gates of heaven?
   Only you have such love for me,
   for you are God.
   So I throw down my earthly idols,
   I remove them from my heart.

1062 Who'd be found worthy *(He alone is worthy)*

Words and Music: Art Bain
arr. Chris Mitchell

1063 Who holds the heavens in his hands?

(Glory to the Lord)

Words and Music: Lynn DeShazo
arr. Chris Mitchell

1. Who holds the hea-vens in his hands?
2. Who holds the right-eous by the hand?

Who made the stars by the word of his pow-er?
Who is the way in this mar-vel-lous hour?

Who put the spi-rit in man and cau-ses all the earth
Who stirs the heart of a man and cau-ses all his saints

to cry out glo-ry?
to cry out glo-ry?

Chorus

Glo-ry to the Lord, wor-ship him, the God of our sal-va-

1064 Who is like him

(Praise Adonai)

Words and Music: Paul Baloche
arr. Chris Mitchell

Verse

Who is like him, the Li - on and the Lamb, seat - ed on the throne? Moun - tains bow down, ev - 'ry o - cean roars to the Lord of hosts.

Chorus

Praise A - do - nai, from the ris - ing of the sun 'til the

The Lord is my light and my salvation –
whom shall I fear?
The Lord is the stronghold of my life –
of whom shall I be afraid?

Psalm 27:1

1065 Who is like our God?

Words and Music: Brian Duane, Brian Doerksen and Brian Thiessen
arr. Chris Mitchell

Who   is   like   our   God?

Who   is   like   our

God?   Ho - ly and
                                                        Migh - ty and

in - ti - mate,   ten - der and strong,
in - no - cent,   jea - lous and kind,

1066 Who is on the Lord's side?

Words: Frances Ridley Havergal

Music: adapted by John Goss

ARMAGEDDON 65 65

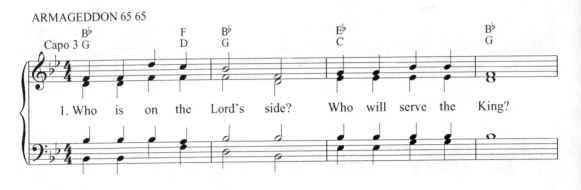

1. Who is on the Lord's side? Who will serve the King?

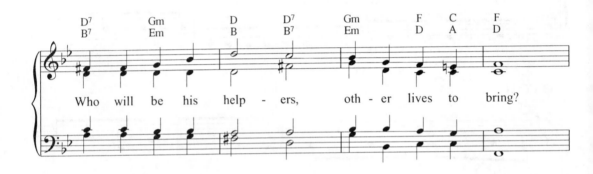

Who will be his help - ers, oth - er lives to bring?

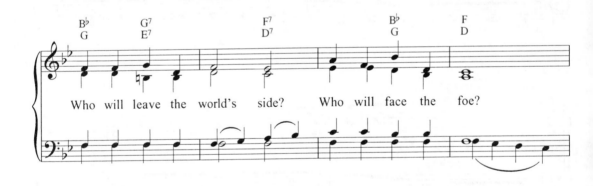

Who will leave the world's side? Who will face the foe?

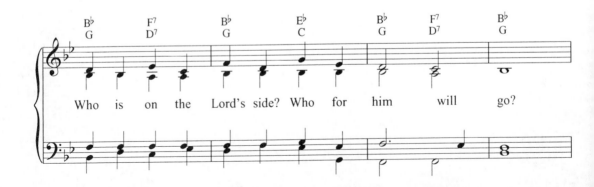

Who is on the Lord's side? Who for him will go?

By thy call of mer-cy, by thy grace di-vine, we are on the Lord's side, Sa-viour, we are thine.

2. Jesus, thou hast bought us
   not with gold or gem,
   but with thine own life-blood,
   for thy diadem.
   With thy blessing filling
   each who comes to thee,
   thou hast made us willing,
   thou hast made us free.
   By thy grand redemption,
   by thy grace divine,
   we are on the Lord's side,
   Saviour, we are thine.

3. Fierce may be the conflict,
   strong may be the foe,
   but the King's own army
   none can overthrow:
   round his standard ranging,
   vict'ry is secure;
   for his truth unchanging
   makes the triumph sure.
   Joyfully enlisting,
   by thy grace divine,
   we are on the Lord's side,
   Saviour, we are thine.

4. Chosen to be soldiers
   in an alien land,
   chosen, called, and faithful,
   for our Captain's band;
   in the service royal
   let us not grow cold,
   let us be right loyal,
   noble, true, and bold.
   Master, thou wilt keep us,
   by thy grace divine,
   always on the Lord's side,
   Saviour, we are thine.

1067 Who is there like Almighty God?

(Strong and mighty)

Words and Music: D. Klassen, T. Klassen, J. Price,
L. Petersen, T. Sampson and S.A. Thompson
arr. Chris Mitchell

1. Who is there like Al - migh - ty God? Je - ho - vah! Je - ho - vah! He is the one who sus - tains all the earth. Je - ho - vah! Je - ho - vah! Gi - ver of breath to all that's a - live. Je - ho - vah! Je - ho - vah!

2. You bring sal - va - tion up - on the earth. Je - ho - vah! Je - ho - vah! At your re - buke all chains will be bro - ken. Je - ho - vah! Je - ho - vah! Ri - ver of hope in a bar - ren land. Je - ho - vah! Je - ho - vah!

1068 Who is this that appears like the dawn?

Words and Music: Michael and Helen Frye

1. Who is this that ap - pears like the dawn?
Fair-er than the moon, bright-er than the sun;
you're the lov-er of my soul. Draw me in - to you,
draw me in - to you.
We will run, we will fly,

2. Who is this that beckons me to come close?
   Beauty beyond words surrounds me when you're near;
   you're the lover of my soul.
   Draw me into you, draw me into you.

3. Who is this that wipes the tears from my eyes?
   Just one glimpse of you steals my heart away;
   you're the lover of my soul.
   Draw me into you, draw me into you.

The righteous cry out, and the Lord hears them;
he delivers them from all their troubles.
The Lord is close to the broken-hearted
and saves those who are crushed in spirit.

Psalm 34:17-18

1069 Who then is this

Words and Music: Matt Spencer

1. Who then is this, that e-ven the wind and the waves o-bey him? Who then is this, says 'Peace, be still' and the storm is o-ver? Mas-ter, Tea-cher, Lord and Sa-viour; Son of God and Son of Man. Lo-ver, Hea-ler, King for e-ver, friend of mine, Em-ma - nu-el.

2. Who then is this, who shat-ters the chains and heals the spi-rit?

1070 Wonderful grace

Words and Music: John Pantry

1. Won-der-ful grace, that gives what I don't de-serve,
pays me what Christ has earned, then lets me go free.
Won-der-ful grace, that gives me the time to change,
wash-es a-way the stains that once co-vered me. And

Chorus

all that I have I lay at the feet of the

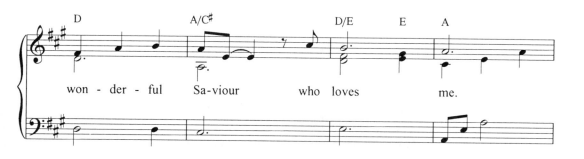

won - der - ful Sa-viour who loves me.

Last time

2. Wonderful grace, that held in the face of death,
   breathed in its latest breath forgiveness for me.
   Wonderful love, whose pow'r can break ev'ry chain,
   giving us life again, setting us free.

Shout with joy to God, all the earth!
Sing the glory of his name;
make his praise glorious!
Say to God. 'How awesome are your deeds!
So great is your power
that your enemies cringe before you.
All the earth bows down to you;
they sing praise to you,
they sing praise to your name.'

Psalm 66:1-4

1071 Worthy, you are worthy

Words and Music: Don Moen

2. Holy, you are holy,
   King of kings, Lord of lords,
   you are holy;
   holy, you are holy,
   King of kings, Lord of lords,
   I worship you.

3. Jesus, you are Jesus,
   King of kings, Lord of lords,
   you are Jesus;
   Jesus, you are Jesus,
   King of kings, Lord of lords,
   I worship you.

1072 Would you be free *(There is power in the blood)*

Words and Music: Lewis E. Jones
arr. Chris Mitchell

1. Would you be free from your bur - den of sin? There's

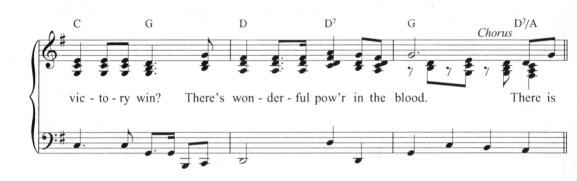

pow'r in the blood, pow'r in the blood; would you, o'er e - vil, a

vic - to - ry win? There's won - der - ful pow'r in the blood. There is

pow'r, pow'r, won - der - work - ing pow'r in the blood of the

Lamb. There is pow'r, pow'r,

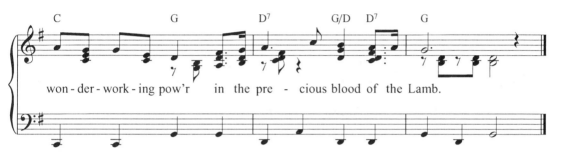

won - der - work - ing pow'r in the pre - cious blood of the Lamb.

2. Would you be free from your passion and pride?
   There's pow'r in the blood, pow'r in the blood;
   come for a cleansing to Calvary's tide.
   There's wonderful pow'r in the blood.

3. Would you be whiter, much whiter than snow?
   There's pow'r in the blood, pow'r in the blood;
   sin stains are lost in its life-giving flow.
   There's wonderful pow'r in the blood.

4. Would you do service for Jesus, your King?
   There's pow'r in the blood, pow'r in the blood;
   would you live daily his praises to sing?
   There's wonderful pow'r in the blood.

1073 Years I spent in vanity and pride　　*(At Calvary)*

Words: William R. Newell

Music: Daniel Brink Towner
arr. Chris Mitchell

1. Years I spent in va - ni - ty and pride, car - ing not my Lord was cru - ci - fied, know - ing not it was for me he died on Cal - va - ry.

Mer - cy there was great and grace was free; par - don there was mul - ti - plied to me; there my bur - dened soul found li - ber - ty, at Cal - va - ry.

2. By God's Word at last my sin I learned;
   then I trembled at the law I'd spurned,
   till my guilty soul imploring turned
   to Calvary.

3. Now I've giv'n to Jesus ev'rything;
   now I gladly own him as my King;
   now my raptured soul can only sing
   of Calvary.

4. O the love that drew salvation's plan!
   O the grace that brought it down to man!
   O the mighty gulf that God did span
   at Calvary!

1074 Ye servants of God

Words: Charles Wesley

Music: Charles Hubert Hastings Parry

LAUDATE DOMINUM (PARRY) 10 10 11 11

2. God ruleth on high, almighty to save;
and still he is nigh, his presence we have;
the great congregation his triumph shall sing,
ascribing salvation to Jesus our King.

3. 'Salvation to God who sits on the throne',
let all cry aloud, and honour the Son:
the praises of Jesus the angels proclaim,
fall down on their faces, and worship the Lamb.

4. Then let us adore, and give him his right —
all glory and pow'r, all wisdom and might:
all honour and blessing, with angels above;
and thanks never-ceasing, and infinite love.

1075 Yes, God is good

Words: John Hampden Gurney

Music: Templi Carmina

WILLIAMS LM

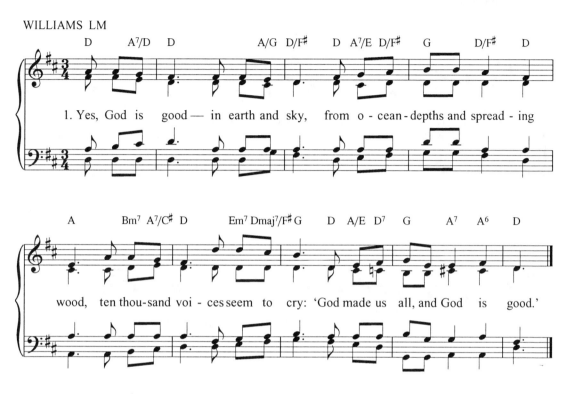

1. Yes, God is good — in earth and sky, from o - cean-depths and spread - ing wood, ten thou-sand voi - ces seem to cry: 'God made us all, and God is good.'

2. The sun that keeps his trackless way
and downward pours his golden flood,
night's sparkling hosts, all seem to say
in accents clear that God is good.

3. The merry birds prolong the strain,
their song with ev'ry spring renewed;
and balmy air and falling rain,
each softly whispers: 'God is good.'

4. We hear it in the rushing breeze;
the hills that have for ages stood,
the echoing sky and roaring seas,
all swell the chorus: 'God is good.'

5. For all thy gifts we bless thee, Lord,
but chiefly for our heav'nly food,
thy pard'ning grace, thy quick'ning word,
these prompt our song, that God is good.

1076 You are a holy God

Words and Music: Brian Duane and Kathryn Scott
arr. Richard Lewis

You are   a ho-ly God,   an all-con-sum-ing fire.
Your ways   are not our ways.   Your thoughts are high a-bove.

You're robed   in maj-es-ty,   bright,
You   are   the foun-tain, Lord,   of

shin-ing as   the sun.
mer-cy, truth   and   love.   And we cry:

'Ho-   ly,   ho-   ly,

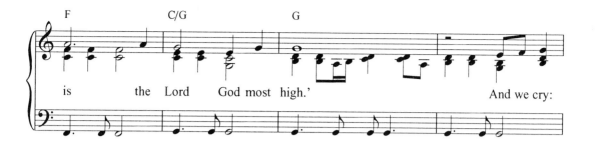

is   the Lord   God most high.'   And we cry:

'Ho -   ly,   ho   -   ly,

is   the Lord   most high'.

It is good to praise the Lord
and make music to your name,
O Most High,
to proclaim your love in the morning
and your faithfulness at night,
to the music of the ten-stringed lyre
and the melody of the harp.
For you make me glad by your deeds, O Lord;
I sing for joy at the work of your hands.

Psalm 92:1-4

1077 You are holy

Words and Music: Reuben Morgan

You are ho - ly, ho - ly, Lord, there is none like you.

You are ho - ly, ho - ly, glo - ry to you a - lone.

You are

I'll sing your prai - ses for e - ver,

deep - er in love with you. Here in your courts where I'm close

to your throne, I've found where I be - long.

1078 You are holy

Words and Music: Scott Wesley Brown

1. You are ho - ly, O Lord, so ho - ly;

you are ho - ly, O Lord, so ho - ly.

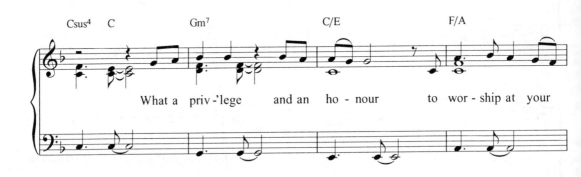

What a priv - 'lege and an ho - nour to wor - ship at your

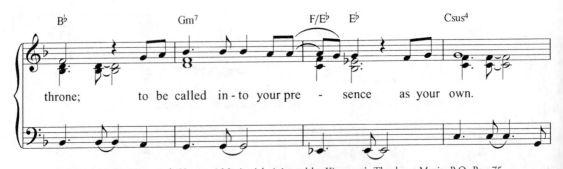

throne; to be called in - to your pre - sence as your own.

2. You are worthy, O Lord, so worthy...

3. You are faithful, O Lord, so faithful...

1079 You are Lord

Words and Music: Ray Chee
arr. Chris Mitchell

You are Lord, mak-er of the hea-vens, you are Lord, rul-er of all na-tions. I lift my voice to wor-ship you, Lord. You are Lord, heal-er and Mes-si-ah, you are Lord, won-der-ful Re-deem-er. I

To you, O Lord, I lift up my soul;
in you I trust, O my God.
Do not let me be put to shame,
nor let my enemies triumph over me.

Psalm 25:1-2

1080 You are my hiding-place

Words and Music: Michael Ledner

This may be sung as a round.

1081 You are my strength when I am weak
(You are my all in all)

Words and Music: Dennis Jernigan

. . . but those who hope in the Lord
will renew their strength.
They will soar on wings like eagles;
they will run and not grow weary,
they will walk and not be faint.

Isaiah 40:31

1082 You are the anchor and foundation

(Never let me go)

Words and Music: David Grant, Carrie Grant and Richard Lewis

Oh, oh, oh,

oh, oh, oh,

oh, oh. 1. You are the

an - chor and foun - da - tion, you are the Rock that will not roll;
King in all your glo - ry, you are the Lamb of vic - to - ry,

1083 You are the breath of life *(The only living God)*

Words and Music: Janine Price
arr. Chris Mitchell

1084 You are the one

Words and Music: Alvin Slaughter
arr. Chris Mitchell

You are the one that makes my feet start danc-ing;
you are the one that drives the dark clouds a-way;
you are the one, you're my rea-son for liv-ing;
you are the one I praise.
I praise you for the ve-ry breath I breathe,

1085 You are the Rose of Sharon *(All the riches of you)*

Words and Music: Shannon J. Wexelberg
arr. Richard Lewis

turn my sor - rows in - to glad - ness,
where I'll wor - ship you for e - ver,

and so much more. You give me all the
my Lord and King.

rich - es of you, you give me all the

rich - es of you. No - thing else on earth

1086 You are the sovereign 'I Am' *(Your name is holy)*

Words and Music: Brian Doerksen

safe-ty with-in, in your ho – ly name.

In your name strength to re-main, to

stand in spite of pain, in your ho – ly name.

CODA

D.C.

Your

name is ho – ly. name is ho – ly.

I will sing of the Lord's great love for ever;
with my mouth I will make your
faithfulness known through all generations.
I will declare that your love stands firm for ever,
that you established your faithfulness in heaven itself.

Psalm 89:1-2

1087 You are warm like the sunshine *(Beautiful God)*

Words and Music: Nigel Hemming
arr. Chris Mitchell

You are warm like the sun-shine on a bright sum-mer day. You are clear as the blue sky when the clouds have rolled a-way. You are gen-tle as the eve-ning breeze that blows a-gainst my face; and I love to be with you, beau-ti-ful God, and I love to be with you, beau-ti-ful God. You pro-

1088 You have been given

Words and Music: Bob Kauflin

wor - ship you.

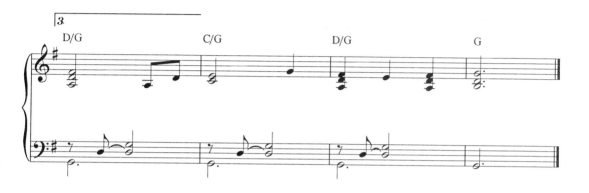

2. We are your people, made for your glory,
and we worship you, yes we worship you.
We are your people, made for your glory,
and we worship you, and we worship you.

3. You have redeemed us from ev'ry nation,
and we worship you, yes we worship you.
You have redeemed us from ev'ry nation,
and we worship you, and we worship you.

1089 You have chosen us   *(We will tell the world)*

Words and Music: Andrew Rayner and Wendy Rayner
arr. Chris Mitchell

You have cho - sen us,   set our lives a - part

to de-clare the won - der of your name.

Awe-some migh - ty God,   Sa - viour, friend and Lord,

of your love and grace we will pro - claim.

1090 You're Messiah

(Messiah)

Words: Jennifer Thune

Music: Ian White

You're Me - si - ah,

you're Mes - si - ah, you're Mes-

si - ah.

1. From all the na - tions we come, we come to your throne
2. Now we lift up ho - ly hands in glo - ri - ous joy
3. We'll spread this pas - sion for you; re - vi - val will flow

1091 You're my rock of refuge

(Rock of refuge)

Words and Music: Gary Sadler
arr. Chris Mitchell

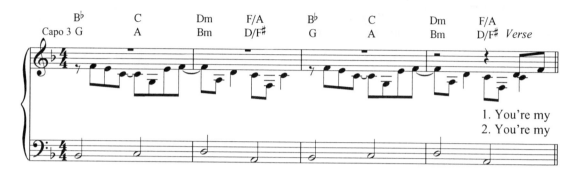

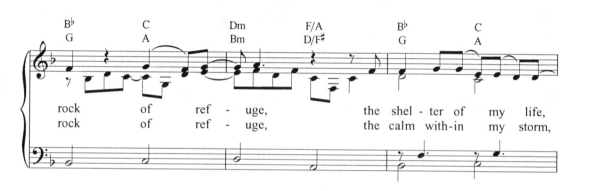

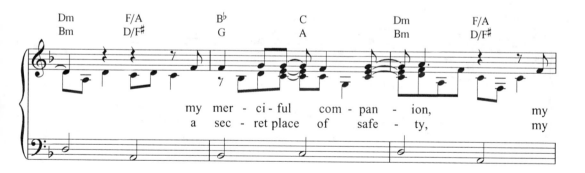

still your love stands guard, O Lord,
through my worst of fears, O Lord,

you are my rock of ref - uge.
you are my rock of ref - uge.

Chorus

And I run to you, and you

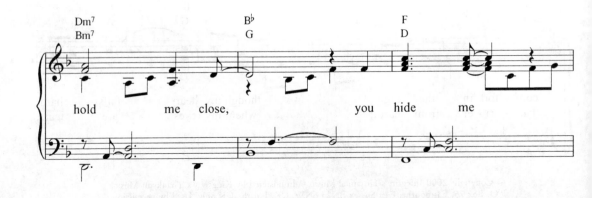

hold me close, you hide me

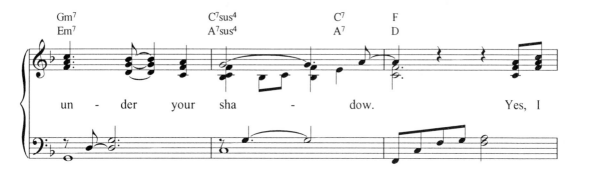

un - der   your   sha -   dow.   Yes, I

run   to you,   it's so good   to know,   O Lord,

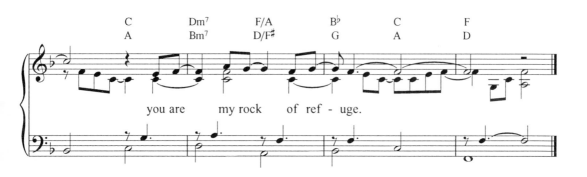

you are   my rock   of ref - uge.

Sing to God, sing praise to his name,
extol him who rides on the clouds –
his name is the Lord –
and rejoice before him.

Psalm 68:4

1092 You're the One who flung the stars

Words and Music: Mark Altrogge

1. You're the One who flung the stars a - cross the hea-
2. You're the One whose bleed - ing head was crowned with thorns,

- vens and you are the One who spoke and moun - tains rose
and in my stead you took God's wrath, and died my death

a - bove the foam - ing seas.
that I might live your life.

You're the One who sends the rain and gold - en sun
And as I fix my gaze on you, I'm cap - ti - va-

1093 Your eye is on the sparrow *(I will run to you)*

Words and Music: Darlene Zschech

1. Your eye is on the spar-row and your hand
   me to your pur-pose, as an-

it com-forts me. From the ends of the earth to the depths
-gels un-der-stand. For your glo - ry may you draw

of my heart, let your mer-cy and strength be seen. 2. You call
all men, as your

love and grace de-mands. And I will run to you,

1094 Your kingdom generation *(Here to eternity)*

Words and Music: Darlene Zschech and David Moyse
arr. Chris Mitchell

1. Your king - dom ge - ne - ra - tion de - clares your maj -
2. We see your Spi - rit mov - ing, we burn with ho -

- es - ty. Our lives are re - sound - ing with your praise.
- ly fire. Your glo - ry is

seen through all the earth.

You set e - ter- -ni - ty in my heart, so I'll live for

1095 Your light broke through my night
(This is how we overcome)

Words and Music: Reuben Morgan

2. Your hand lifted me up,
   I stand on higher ground.
   Your praise rose in my heart,
   and made this valley sing.

Give thanks to the Lord, for he is good.
His love endures for ever.
Give thanks to the God of gods.
His love endures for ever.
Give thanks to the Lord of lords:
His love endures for ever.

Psalm 136:1-3

1096 Your love is amazing

(Hallelujah)

Words and Music: Brian Doerksen and Brenton Brown
arr. Chris Mitchell

1. Your love is a - maz - ing, stea - dy and un - chang -
   - ing, I can feel it ris -

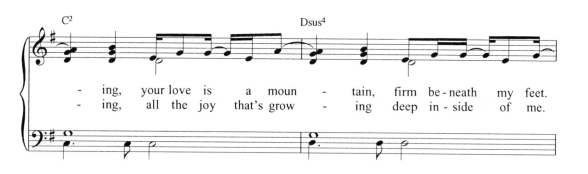

- ing, your love is a moun - tain, firm be - neath my feet.
- ing, all the joy that's grow - ing deep in - side of me.

Your love is a mys - t'ry, how you gent - ly lift
Ev - 'ry time I see you, all your good - ness shines

me, when I am sur - round - ed, your love car - ries me.
through, I can feel this God - song, ris - ing up in me.

Chorus

Hal - le - lu - jah, hal - le - lu -

- jah, hal - le - lu - jah,

your love makes me sing. Hal - le - lu - jah, hal - le - lu -

- jah, hal - le - lu - jah, your love makes me sing.

1.

Last time *Fine*

2. Your love is sur - pris -

Yes, you make me sing.

Lord, you make me sing, sing, sing.

How you make me sing. Hal - le - lu -

1097 Your only Son

(Lamb of God)

Words and Music: Twila Paris
arr. Chris Mitchell

1. Your on-ly Son, no sin to hide, but you have

sent him from your side to walk up-on this gui-ty

sod, and to be-come the Lamb of God. O Lamb of

God, sweet Lamb of God; I love the ho-ly Lamb of God. O wash me

in his pre-cious blood. My Je - sus Christ, the Lamb of God.

2. Your gift of love they crucified,
   they laughed and scorned him as he died;
   the humble King they named a fraud,
   and sacrificed the Lamb of God.

3. I was so lost I should have died,
   but you have brought me to your side
   to be led by your staff and rod,
   and to be called a lamb of God.

1098 Your words of life *(Burn in my heart again)*

Words and Music: Andrew Bromley

1. Your words of life burn in my soul, I feel this hun-ger more and more, com-pell-ing me to fol-low you, call-ing me to walk in truth. To walk in ways of right-eous-ness, to long and crave for ho-li-ness, to live my life in pu-ri-ty, to give my life up will-

2. Your Spirit like a fire in me,
I feel this passion stirring me,
compassion's fire, this flame of love,
could only be from God above.
Open my eyes, my pray'r, O Lord,
to see the hungry, thirsty soul.
Reach out my hand to meet the need
to give your love so selflessly.

Praise the Lord, O my soul;
all my inmost being, praise his holy name.
Praise the Lord, O my soul,
and forget not all his benefits –
who forgives all your sins
and heals all your diseases . . .

Psalm 103:1-3

1099 You said

Words and Music: Reuben Morgan

1. You said 'Ask and you will re-ceive what-e-ver you need.'

You said 'Pray, and I'll hear from hea-ven

and I'll heal your land.'

2. You said your glo-ry will fill the earth like wa-ter the sea.

You said 'Lift up your eyes, the

har-vest is here, the king-dom is here.' You said 'Ask, and I'll give the na-

- tions to you.' O Lord, that's the cry of my heart.

Dis-tant shores and the is - lands will see your light as it ri -

Indexes

Index of Songwriters, Authors, Composers and Arrangers

Scriptural Index

GENESIS

EXODUS

LEVITICUS

NUMBERS

DEUTERONOMY

JOSHUA

1 SAMUEL

2 SAMUEL

1 KINGS

1 CHRONICLES

2 CHRONICLES

EZRA

NEHEMIAH

JOB

PROVERBS

SONG OF SOLOMON

ISAIAH

JOHN

Key Word Index

The key word categories appear alphabetically and are cross-referenced to make it as easy as possible for worship leaders to find songs and hymns suitable for various themes and occasions.

Index of First Lines and Titles

● the source 2 Guitarists' Edition

1470112   1 84003 725 3

⬤ the source Music Edition

1470104   1 84003 120 4

● the source Guitarists' Edition

1470110　　　　　　　1 84003 287 1